The Monkey King

Wu Ch'êng-ên

Originally translated by Arthur Waley

Abridged by Alison Waley

Level 4

Retold by Coleen Degnan-Veness

Series Editors: Andy Hopkins and Jocelyn Potter

Pearson Education Limited
Edinburgh Gate, Harlow,
Essex CM20 2JE, England
and Associated Companies throughout the world.

ISBN: 978-1-4082-3206-4

This edition first published by Pearson Education Ltd 2010

1 3 5 7 9 10 8 6 4 2

Text copyright © Pearson Education Ltd 2010

Illustrations by Mike McKeever

The moral rights of the authors have been asserted in accordance with
the Copyright Designs and Patents Act 1988

Set in 11/13pt A. Garamond
Printed in China
SWTC/01

Acknowledgements

The Publishers would like to thank Michael Dean for his work on the previous Penguin Readers edition
of this title.
We are grateful to the following for permission to reproduce photographs:
(Key: b-bottom; c-centre; l-left; r-right; t-top)
iStockphoto: Christopher Russell 90; **Photolibrary.com**: National Geographic 91b; Stockbyte 91t

All other images © Pearson Education
Picture research by Frances Topp

Every effort has been made to trace the copyright holders and we apologise in
advance for any unintentional omissions. We would be pleased to insert the
appropriate acknowledgement in any subsequent edition of this publication.

Published by Pearson Education Ltd in association with Penguin Books Ltd, both
companies being subsidiaries of Pearson Plc

For a complete list of the titles available in the Penguin Active Reading series please write to your local
Pearson Longman office or to: Penguin Readers Marketing Department, Pearson Education,
Edinburgh Gate, Harlow, Essex CM20 2JE, England.

Contents

1.1 What's the book about?

Look at the picture on the front of this book. Talk to another student.

1 Have you read stories about the Monkey King? Have you seen films or television programmes about him? What kind of story do you think this is?

2 Which words in the box describe these events or characters in the story, do you think? Write them next to the pictures.

> brave clever dangerous entertaining difficult magic
> powerful violent

1 ....

2 ....

3 ....

4 ....

5 ....

6 ....

7 ....

8 ....

1.2 What happens first?

Read the title of Chapter 1 and the sentences in *italics* under it. Then look at the pictures in this chapter and discuss these questions.

1 Is Monkey a human or an animal?

2 What does Monkey use to make more monkeys?

3 What else can Monkey do?

4 Who teaches him?

5 Will you read about strange gods or normal families?

6 Who or what are the characters on page 14?

Monkey's Story

Monkey pulled out some hairs from his chest and, crying 'Change!', threw them into the air. At once, they became several hundred small monkeys.

From the beginning of time, the rock was smoothed and cleaned by Heaven and Earth, by the strong sun and the gentle moon, until one day it broke into two pieces and gave birth to a stone egg, about as big as a child's ball. From the egg came a stone **monkey**.

At once, this monkey learned to climb and run. But first, it looked north and south and east and west. As it looked, a strange light came from its eyes. The light shone as far as the **Jade Emperor**, who sat in the Cloud Palace of the Golden Gates. The Jade Emperor asked his ministers to open the gate of the Southern Heaven and look out at the light.

'This light,' reported the ministers, 'comes from the small country of Ao-lai, to the east of the Mountain of Flowers and Fruit.'

And in the country of Ao-lai, the monkey ran and jumped. He picked flowers, ate grass and fruit, and drank from streams and rivers. His friends were all the animals of that country, and the other monkeys were his family. At night, he slept among the rocks and in the day he walked through the **caves**.

One day, the monkeys were washing in a stream when one of them spoke. 'None of us knows where this stream comes from. Let's follow it and find out.' So they all ran up the stream until they came to a great waterfall.

The monkeys shouted, 'Lovely water, lovely water! It starts in a mountain cave and runs all the way to the Great Sea. Who can find the place where the water comes from? If one of us could find this place and return safely, we would make him our king!'

'I will go!' shouted the Stone Monkey. 'I will go!'

Look at him! He shuts his eyes, and with one big jump he passes through the curtain of water. But there is no water where he has landed. Instead he finds a great, shining iron bridge in front of him.

Monkey walked along the bridge and came to a cave. Outside the cave there was a sign: *This Cave of the Water Curtain in the Country of the Mountain of Flowers and Fruit Leads to Heaven.*

Monkey laughed and jumped with happiness. He ran back across the bridge, shut his eyes and jumped through the waterfall to the other monkeys.

---

monkey /ˈmʌŋki/ (n) a small tree-climbing animal with a long tail
jade /dʒeɪd/ (n) a valuable green stone which is used in jewellery
emperor /ˈempərə/ (n) the ruler of a large area, of many countries
cave /keɪv/ (n) a deep hole inside a mountain

'Good news!' he shouted. 'Good news! Come with me, all of you!'

They followed the Stone Monkey to the Cave of the Water Curtain. There the Stone Monkey sat down and talked to them.

'Gentlemen!' he said. 'I have been through the waterfall and have come back again. I have given you a home in this cave, so am I not your king now?'

The monkeys **bowed** to the Stone Monkey and they all cried, 'Great King for a thousand years!' The Stone Monkey became the Monkey King and he made other monkeys his ministers.

And all the monkeys were happy. During the day they walked and played on the Mountain of Flowers and Fruit, and at night they slept in the Cave of the Water Curtain. They had everything they wanted. Their lives were complete.

The Monkey King enjoyed this simple life for several hundred years. But one day at a great party with all the other monkeys, he suddenly started to cry.

The other monkeys all bowed, saying, 'Why is our king so sad?'

'Today,' said the Monkey King, 'I am not sad. But I am worried about the future. Sadly, the time will come when I will become old and weak. Yama, King of Death, is waiting to destroy me. I do not want to be born again on Earth. How can I live for all time among the people of the sky?'

The monkeys all started to cry, each thinking of his own **mortality**. One of them said, 'Only Buddhas and Immortals do not go to Yama, King of Death. Only they live forever.'

'Where can I find these Immortals?' asked the Monkey King.

bow /baʊ/ (v/n) to bend at the waist with your head down, as a sign of politeness
mortality /mɔːˈtæləti/ (n) the state of being human and having to die. A mortal is someone who is unable to live forever.

2

'Here on Earth they live in very old caves far to the West.'

'Tomorrow,' said the Monkey King, 'I shall say goodbye to you. I shall go down the mountain and travel to the end of the world. I want to learn to live for all time and to escape from death.'

Next morning, he walked to the sea and sailed in a boat to the borders of the Southern World. There he climbed out on to the beach. And then he walked and walked, through towns and cities, to the West.

On the way, he learned to wear clothes and to behave like a human. But he met humans who wanted only to be rich and famous. He met nobody who worried about his mortality.

One day, he came to the Western Ocean, where he built another boat. Then he sailed to the Western Continent, where he saw a very high and beautiful wooded mountain. At the top of the mountain was the Cave of the Moon and Three Stars, where the Immortal Subodhi lived.

Monkey at once bowed and touched the ground with his head three times.

'Where do you come from?' asked the Immortal.

'I am from the Cave of the Water Curtain,' said Monkey, 'on the Mountain of Flowers and Fruit in the country of Ao-lai.'

'That is impossible!' shouted the Immortal. 'Between there and here are two oceans and the whole of the Southern Continent. You are lying!'

'I have sailed across the oceans and walked over the continents for more than ten years,' said Monkey. 'At last I have reached here.'

Monkey told the Immortal how he had come from a magic stone. The Immortal thought that Monkey was a natural product of Heaven and Earth, so he agreed to teach him. Monkey jumped up and down with happiness.

Day after day, he and the other students learned to speak and behave correctly. They learned to write well and to study the Scriptures*. When they were not studying, the students grew flowers and trees. They lit fires and fetched water. And so Monkey lived in this way for six or seven years.

Finally, the Immortal sent for Monkey late one night because he wanted to teach him the Way of Long Life.

'Come close and listen carefully,' said the Immortal.

Monkey went down on his knees on the floor at the Immortal's feet, listening carefully. The Immortal **recited** a magic poem with many lines. The words shook Monkey's **soul** and he was never the same Monkey again. He thanked the Immortal many times, because now he knew the Way of Long Life.

* Scriptures: the books of a religion

recite /rɪ'saɪt/ (v) to say something from memory so that everyone can hear you
soul /səʊl/ (n) the part of a person that is not the body. In some religions, it is believed to be the most important part of a person.

Time passed quickly and three years later the Immortal again invited Monkey to his room, where he taught him seventy-two **transformations**. Monkey was a quick learner and he practised until he could change himself into something else, using all seventy-two ways.

One day, when the Immortal and his students were in front of the cave admiring the evening view, the Immortal spoke to Monkey. 'Monkey, how much have you learned?'

'Thanks to you,' said Monkey, 'I have learned a lot. In addition to changing myself into other forms, I can already fly.'

'Let me see you do it,' said the Immortal.

Monkey put his feet together, jumped twenty metres into the air and rode the clouds for a few minutes. Then he dropped to the ground, saying, 'You see, I can ride the clouds.'

'That is not riding the clouds,' said the Immortal, laughing. 'A real cloud-rider can start in the morning from the Northern Sea, cross the Eastern, the Western and the Southern Seas and land again in one day.'

'It sounds very difficult,' said Monkey.

'Nothing in the world is difficult,' said the Immortal. 'Only our own thoughts make things seem difficult. Now I will teach you to fly from one continent to another.'

The other students laughed, saying, 'If Monkey flies all that way, he will be able to earn a living as a postman.'

transformation /ˌtrænsfəˈmeɪʃən/ (n) a complete change of form; from a person to an animal, for example

But Monkey spent all night practising what the Immortal had taught him. By morning he could fly wherever he wanted.

One summer day, some students were sitting under a tree. A student said, 'Monkey, why do you deserve private teaching by the Immortal? Has he taught you the transformations, by all the seventy-two ways?'

'I have been working on them day and night and now I can do them all,' said Monkey.

'Could you show us?'

Proudly, Monkey made a magic sign, said some magic words and transformed himself into a tree.

'Well done, Monkey, well done!' shouted the other students. They all laughed.

The Immortal heard their laughter and he came running out from the cave. 'Who is making all this noise?' he asked.

Monkey changed himself back from a tree to a monkey. He sat with the students again and said, 'Immortal, we are practising our lessons out here.'

'You were all shouting and laughing!' said the Immortal, angrily. 'I want to know why.'

Then one student said, 'Monkey was transforming himself into a tree, just for fun.'

'You, Monkey, come here!' shouted the Immortal. 'Why do you think I taught you these secrets of life? So you can make other people laugh?'

'I am very sorry,' said Monkey.

'I will not punish you,' said the Immortal. 'But you cannot stay here. You must leave us.'

Monkey started to cry. 'Where can I go?' he asked.

'Go back to where you came from. Go as quickly as you can. Never tell anyone that you were a student of mine. I am sure that no good will come of your life.'

And so poor Monkey said goodbye to everybody. He flew back to the Eastern Sea and his home in the Cave of the Water Curtain on the Mountain of Flowers and Fruit.

'Little ones,' shouted the Monkey King, 'I have come back!'

At once, big and small monkeys **leapt** out of trees with cries of 'Long live our King!' Then, pushing each other to get near him, they cried, 'Why did you go for so long? We have been watching for your return day after day! While you were away, a **demon** took our cave and everything we own and many of our children. Now we dare not sleep, night or day.'

'What demon dares to do this?' cried Monkey. 'I will make him pay!'

'King, he is called the Destroying Demon, and he lives north of here. But he comes and goes like a cloud, like wind, like rain, like thunder and lightning, so we do not know where his home is or how far away.'

'Well, don't worry,' said Monkey. 'I will go and look for him.'

Dear Monkey! He leapt into the sky and soon saw in front of him a high mountain and a cave, where the Destroying Demon was waiting for him.

'Where is the owner of the Cave of the Water Curtain?' cried the Demon.

'You have such large eyes,' shouted Monkey, 'but you cannot see Monkey?'

'Oh! You are not half a metre high! If I killed such a small **creature** with my **sword**, I would look foolish.'

So the two of them fought with their hands and feet, hitting and kicking each other. Soon the Demon was fighting like a wild animal. Monkey pulled out some hairs from his chest and, crying 'Change!', threw them into the air. At once, they became several hundred small monkeys.

See how the monkeys jump on the Demon, pulling and hitting him. Then Monkey takes up the Demon's great sword and brings it down on his head, breaking it in two. Then, by his magic, he transforms all the monkeys back into hairs.

leap /li:p/ (v/n) to jump high and far
demon /ˈdiːmən/ (n) a very bad and dangerous ghost
creature /ˈkriːtʃə/ (n) a living being: a person or animal, but not a plant
sword /sɔːd/ (n) a very long, sharp knife used, especially in the past, for fighting

When Monkey returned home to the cave on the Mountain of Flowers and Fruit, he brought the great sword of the Destroying Demon, and he amused the other monkeys by teaching them to make **weapons** of wood.

Then, one day, the Monkey King called all the other monkeys to him.

'All this,' he said, pointing to their wooden weapons, 'is only a game. We cannot defend ourselves from a real enemy with these.'

'We know a city that is full of soldiers. They must have plenty of weapons,' the others said. They quickly told Monkey where it was.

'Stay here and amuse yourselves,' Monkey said. 'I will see what I can do.'

Dear Monkey! Using his magic, he flew to the city and, with his breath, blew such a strong wind that all the people locked themselves indoors. This was his chance. He found where the weapons were kept, kicked down the door, and changed his hairs into thousands of small monkeys who took the weapons. Carried on a magic wind, they were soon back at the cave.

The monkeys learned to use the weapons, and all sorts of wild animals and demon kings began to call Monkey their king.

But Monkey found his own weapon too heavy, so he went to the **Dragon** of the Eastern Sea in search of something lighter. The Dragon King welcomed him to the palace, with his dragon children, dragon grandchildren and fish soldiers.

weapon /ˈwepən/ (n) something that can be used to fight with
dragon /ˈdræɡən/ (n) a large imaginary animal with wings, which has the power to breathe out fire

7

Monkey made his request, and a fish soldier brought out a great sword.
'Too heavy,' said Monkey.
More fish soldiers brought out an enormous fork.
'Too light,' said Monkey.
The dragon mother and her daughter came from a back room in the palace and suggested their magic iron **cudgel**.
'The Gods used it when they decided how deep the rivers and the seas should be,' said the Dragon King. He agreed that Monkey should have it.
When it was brought, Monkey saw that it was a thick piece of iron six metres long. He used his magic to bring it down to less than a metre. Then he waved it over his head, striking terror into everybody in the room.
But now he demanded something to wear, to go with the weapon, and this was too much. A pair of cloud-stepping shoes, a **cap** of red gold and a coat of light metal were brought to him, but the angry Dragon King also sent for his brothers from the Southern, Northern and Western Seas and told them about Monkey's many requests.
The Dragon of the South was angry. 'Put him in prison!' he cried.
'No, no,' warned the Dragon King. 'We cannot go near him now. If he touches us with that iron cudgel, he will kill us. Let him keep the clothes. We will complain to Heaven, and Heaven will punish him.'
Monkey took the clothes, but he knew that they were going to complain about him.

cudgel /ˈkʌdʒəl/ (n) a short, thick heavy stick used to fight others
cap /kæp/ (n) a cover for your head, like a hat

Soon after that, the Jade Emperor received the complaint from the Dragon of the Eastern Sea.

'How long,' the Jade Emperor asked his ministers, 'has this Monkey existed, and why does he behave like an Immortal?'

'In the last three hundred years, he has learned a lot,' said a minister. 'Let's give him work here in Heaven where we will be able to watch him.'

This suggestion pleased the Jade Emperor, and a minister was sent to bring Monkey to Heaven. Monkey tidied his clothes, told the older monkeys to look after the younger ones, and followed the minister to Heaven.

'I am going to give you a job,' said the Jade Emperor to Monkey. 'You are going to look after the Apple Garden.'

Monkey was very happy and ran to the Apple Garden to start work. He was told that on the outer side of the garden were special apples. They were ready to eat once in three thousand years. If you ate one of these, you would become wise, with strong arms and legs and a light body. In the middle were trees with apples that were ready to eat once in six thousand years. If you ate these, you would go up in the air and stay there, and would never grow old. At the back were trees with apples that were ready to eat once in nine thousand years. If you ate these, you would live longer than Heaven and Earth.

Monkey was very happy with this information. He watched the trees closely, making up his mind to eat the fruit before anybody else got a chance.

Soon, noticing that some apples were ready to eat, he sent his helpers away. He climbed into a high tree and ate until he could eat no more.

When the Queen of Heaven sent her lady assistants for apples, they were turned away at the gates by Monkey's helpers. 'We must ask the Monkey King first,' they said. 'He is resting in one of the trees.'

But when they came to the tree, they found only Monkey's cap and shoes. They could not see him. In fact, Monkey had made himself five centimetres long and was asleep under a leaf.

The Queen of Heaven's lady assistants picked three basketfuls from each of the first two groups of trees. When they came to the third, they found just one apple. When one of the ladies tried to pick it, Monkey woke up. At once, he changed back to his true size.

'Who are you?' shouted Monkey.

The lady assistants went down on their knees. 'Monkey King, don't be angry. We were sent by the Queen and we could not find you. Please forgive us.'

'Get up from your knees,' said Monkey, his voice full of kindness. 'I have heard that the Queen of Heaven is having a **banquet**. Can you tell me who is invited?'

banquet /ˈbæŋkwɪt/ (n) a formal dinner for many people for a special person or occasion

Monkey was told that all the Immortals, Emperors of the Four Quarters and Gods of the seas and hills would be there. He immediately asked, 'Will I be invited?'

'I have not heard,' said one of the lady assistants. 'We do not know.'

'Quite right, ladies,' said Monkey. 'Just wait here while I go and see.'

Dear Monkey! He recited some magic lines, crying 'Stay, stay, stay!' The lady assistants were suddenly unable to move while he went off on his magic cloud.

No one had arrived at the banquet yet, but Monkey could smell the food and wine. He sent the servants to sleep by magic. Look at them, how their hands fall to their sides, their heads drop on to their chests, their eyes close! Monkey then took some of the finest and best of the food and drank glass after glass of wine until he was quite drunk.

'Bad! Bad!' he thought to himself. 'I will certainly get into trouble, so I will go home and sleep.'

But it was too late for that.

Back at the Apple Garden, the Queen's ladies were finally saved. They reported that the Monkey King had eaten many of the biggest apples and had now disappeared.

When the great Goddess Kuan-yin arrived for the banquet, she found half the food eaten and all the wine gone. When the servants were woken, they explained that the Monkey King had sent them to sleep. That was the last time

they had seen the food and the wine. The Jade Emperor was informed and he sent heavenly soldiers to find Monkey.

Monkey was burned in fire for nine days, and at the end of it his eyes were red but he was still alive. He was attacked with swords and the Gods of Thunder threw thunder at him. But nothing could destroy him.

In the end, hearing of this situation, the great Buddha himself arrived and called Monkey to him. 'How long ago,' he asked him, 'did you try to become an Immortal and learn the things that make you dare behave like this?'

Monkey at once recited:

Born of Earth and Sky, I am a magic Immortal.
I am an old monkey from the Mountain of Flowers and Fruit;
In the Cave of the Water Curtain, I work and laugh and play.
I found a friend and teacher who taught me the Great Secret;
I made myself perfect in the Ways of Immortality,
I learned transformations without limit or end,
I tired of the narrow world of men, and lived in the Jade Heaven.
But why should Heaven's palace have only one emperor?
On Earth king follows king, as the strong bow to the stronger.
Only a hero fights with the Gods of Gods.

That was what Monkey recited. Buddha laughed. 'But you are only a monkey-**spirit**,' he said. 'The Jade Emperor has been making himself perfect for countless years. How can you hope to take his place and become emperor yourself? You are only an animal that looks half human! Talk no more of this.'

'Why should he be emperor for all time? Tell him to go and to give me my chance,' said Monkey. 'That is all I ask. And if he will not, I will see that he never has any peace.'

'What magic have you got that would help you to take Heaven for yourself?'

'I have a lot of magic,' replied Monkey. 'I can jump through the clouds from continent to continent. Am I not good enough to live in the palaces of Heaven?'

Buddha said, 'If you are really so clever, you will sit here in my right hand and then jump off. If you succeed, you can become the Jade Emperor. But if you fail, you will go back to Earth and you will be punished for centuries.'

Monkey thought, 'This Buddha is a complete fool. How could I fail to jump off his hand!'

Buddha held out his hand, which looked about the size of a large leaf.

Monkey took the magic iron cudgel that the Dragon King had given him, and that he had transformed into a stick the size of a needle. He put it behind his ear and then he jumped from the hand as far and as fast as he could.

spirit /ˈspɪrɪt/ (n) a dead person or animal's form when it visits the living

He was flying very fast, but Buddha watched him with the eye of **wisdom**. Monkey came at last to five high pink **towers**.

'This must be the end of the world,' said Monkey to himself. 'Now I will return to Buddha, become emperor, and all Heaven will be mine. But I had better leave some sign that I was here.'

Pulling out a hair, he changed it into a writing-brush heavy with ink, and at the bottom of the middle tower he wrote: *The great Monkey King reached this place.* Then he jumped back to where he had come from.

Standing on Buddha's hand, he said, 'I have gone and I have returned. You can tell the Jade Emperor that his job is mine.'

'You smelly creature,' said Buddha, 'you have been on my hand all the time.'

'You are completely wrong,' said Monkey. 'I travelled to the end of the world, saw five pink towers and wrote on one of them. Would you like me to take you and show you?'

'No need,' said Buddha. 'Just look down.'

Monkey looked down, with his eyes still red from the nine days of fire. There, at the bottom of the middle finger of Buddha's hand, he saw the words *The great Monkey King reached this place.*

Monkey could not speak and his red eyes opened wide in surprise. At last he

wisdom /ˈwɪzdəm/ (n) great knowledge that comes from experience or learning
tower /ˈtaʊə/ (n) a tall building, or part of a building that is taller than the rest

said, 'Impossible! Impossible! I wrote that on a tower going high into the sky. How did it get on the Buddha's finger? It is magic! I shall go back to look!'

Dear Monkey! He was preparing to jump again when Buddha pushed him out of the Western Gate of Heaven. As he did, he changed his five fingers into Metal, Wood, Water, Fire and Earth. They became a mountain which pressed poor Monkey down with its great weight.

The name *Mountain of Metal, Wood, Water, Fire and Earth* was written on a large rock on the mountain. Under the mountain there was enough air for Monkey to breathe, but no opening which Monkey's head or hand could squeeze through.

Buddha then told a spirit to look after Monkey and give him food and drink.

'And when the days of his punishment are finished,' said Buddha, 'a man will come here and save him.'

Time passed, and then one day the Buddha said to his followers, 'I have noticed a lot of difference between the people who live in the four continents of the world. The people in the East are polite, peaceful and cheerful. People in the North are lazy and stupid, so do little harm. In our Western Continent, there is no killing, although there is little real wisdom. But in the South, they are greedy and murderous. A knowledge of the True Scriptures might improve them.'

'Do you have these Scriptures?' asked his followers.

'Yes, three baskets of them,' said Buddha. 'One speaks of Heaven, another of Earth, and a third can save people from the Wrong Way. These are the path to perfection, the only gate to the True Way. But down in the real world, people are so stupid that they laugh at them. I need to find someone who will go to the Eastern land. There he might find a believer who could come here from China. I would give this believer the Scriptures to take back to China and change the hearts of the people.'

The Goddess Kuan-yin came forward and bowed three times.

'I would like to go to the Eastern land and find someone to fetch the Scriptures.'

'Who would be better than you!' said Buddha.

So Kuan-yin called her bodyguard, Hui-yen, who carried a great iron cudgel, and they started at once.

After they had travelled a long way, they came to the River of Sands. There, a horribly ugly creature leapt out of the water and began a terrible fight with the bodyguard.

Suddenly, the creature stopped fighting, looked hard at the bodyguard and asked, 'Who dares to fight with me? Surely I have seen you before in the gardens of the Goddess Kuan-yin?'

'The Goddess herself is here, in front of you,' Hui-yen replied.

'I ask you to forgive me!' cried the creature. 'I am not really the ugly creature that you see. I was given this horrible shape as a punishment for a crime that I did in Heaven. I was sent to the world below, where I am always hungry and I must attack travellers and eat them.'

'But you are adding new crimes on Earth to your crime in Heaven by killing people,' said the Goddess Kuan-yin. 'Why not come with us? If our journey is successful, you will be forgiven and allowed to return to Heaven.'

'I would gladly go back,' the creature answered. 'But I have eaten so many humans. Even now, nine heads are lying on the waters of the River of Sands. I have played games with them and I do not think I will be allowed back into Heaven after that.'

'Don't be silly,' she replied. 'Take the heads and hang them round your neck. I shall make you a **priest** and give you the name "Sandy Priest". Wait here and never again take a human life. You will see that a man will come this way. He will be looking for the Scriptures and a good use will be found for the nine heads.'

So the Goddess and her bodyguard continued their journey and came to a high mountain with a most horrible smell. A dirty, smelly, pig-like creature leapt out and attacked Kuan-yin

priest /priːst/ (n) a person with religious duties who performs at religious events

with a great fork and fought hard with her bodyguard.

For safety, Kuan-yin stood in the sky above them and then threw down flowers, which fell between the bodyguard's cudgel and the fork.

'Fighting with flowers?' cried the pig. 'What kind of priest are you?'

'The great Goddess Kuan-yin threw them down on us from her cloud, where she is standing,' replied the bodyguard.

At once, the pig bowed to the sky. 'Forgive me, Goddess, forgive me! I am not really a pig at all. For a crime in Heaven, the Jade Emperor sent me down here.'

'This is a chance for you,' said Kuan-yin. 'We are on our way to China to look for a man who will collect the Scriptures. If you went with him to India, we would forgive all your crimes.'

'I will! I will!' the pig-like creature shouted.

So they gave him the name of Pigsy, and left him to watch for the **pilgrim** who would collect the Scriptures.

The Goddess and her bodyguard went on their way and soon they met a dragon who had fought against the Gods.

'Can you help me?' the dragon cried out.

Kuan-yin went back to Heaven. She asked the Gods to forgive the dragon if he would transform himself into a white horse and carry the pilgrim to India.

Continuing their journey, the Goddess and her bodyguard suddenly saw a mountain covered in magic fog and lit by golden light from Heaven. They recognised it at once as the mountain which covered the Monkey King.

Kuan-yin looked sad and recited:

Long ago he was purposelessly brave.
In his blackness of heart he spoiled the Heavenly Apple Banquet
And tried to take the place of the Jade Emperor.
Will he ever again be free and win back his name?

Then came a voice from inside the mountain: 'Who is reciting a list of my crimes?'

Kuan-yin found the spirit who looked after Monkey. This spirit led her to Monkey's prison under the mountain, which was a kind of stone box.

Monkey looked out through a thin opening with his red eyes and cried, 'You are the Goddess Kuan-yin! Why have you come here? Buddha tricked me and I have sat in this little box for five hundred years. But I am very sorry for the things I have done and now I want to do good in the world.'

Kuan-yin was very happy. 'Just wait quietly here until I return with my pilgrim and he will save you,' she said.

And so they left Monkey and went on to the East, to find the pilgrim.

pilgrim /ˈpɪlgrɪm/ (n) a person who travels a long way to a place that is important to their religion

2.1 Were you right?

Think back to your answers to Activity 1.2 on page iv. Then find the right endings to these sentences. Circle **a** or **b**.

1 In Ao-lai, all Monkey's friends and family are ...

    a animals.   **b** humans.

2 In the Cave of the Moon and Three Stars, Monkey entertains ...

    a the other monkeys.   **b** the Immortal.

3 To transform himself into other things, Monkey uses ...

    a his cudgel.   **b** his magic powers.

4 Kuan-yin and buddha are ...

    a gods.   **b** demons.

5 Sandy and Pigsy agree to help Kuan-yin because they hope for ...

    a payment.   **b** forgiveness.

2.2 What more did you learn?

Match the sentences below with the pictures.

1 the Jade Emperor

2 the Dragon King

3 Kuan-yin

4 Buddha

5 Sandy

6 Pigsy

a He punishes Monkey by putting him under a mountain.

b He has nine heads from the men he has eaten.

c He loses a fight that is won with flowers.

d He gives Monkey a job in Heaven.

e She offers to find someone to take the Scriptures to China.

f He gives Monkey an iron cudgel.

2.3 Language in use

Read the sentences in the box. Then find the correct endings to the sentences below. Write a–f.

> **If he touches** us with that iron cudgel, **he will kill** us.
>
> **If you ate** one of these, **you would become** wise..

1 ☐ If one of us found the mountain cave, ...

2 ☐ If I killed such a small creature with my sword, ...

3 ☐ If the Emperor will not give me a chance, ...

4 ☐ If you ate the apples at the back of the garden, ...

5 ☐ If our journey is successful, ...

6 ☐ If you went to India, ...

a you will be forgiven.

b we would forgive all your crimes.

c we would make him our king.

d you would live longer than Heaven and Earth.

e I would look foolish.

f he will never have any peace.

2.4 What happens next?

Read the title of Chapter 2 and look at the pictures. Who is the pilgrim who is going to save Monkey? What do you think? Tick (✓) two pictures.

The Journey Begins

'I can tell you that I have killed quite a lot of people. And I am still the great Monkey King!' answered Monkey.

At a time when the great and very old city of Ch'ang-an was the capital of China, there was an examination to find the cleverest men in the country. These men would do the work of the government.

A man by the name of Ch'en O decided to try his luck at the examination, as it was his mother's wish. Arriving late, he found that the examination had begun. But to his surprise, he won first place and he received a letter signed by the Emperor.

In those days, the winner of first place in the examination was led through the streets on horseback. And by chance, on that day, the only daughter of a minister sat in her high tower with a ball in her hand. Seeing the handsome Ch'en riding by, and knowing of his success in the examination, she threw the ball cleverly on to his hat. This was how a lady chose her husband.

No time was wasted. Ch'en and the minister's daughter were married, and hand in hand they went into the bedroom as man and wife. Early next morning, Ch'en was made Governor of Chiang-chou and, as he was told to begin work at once, he started on the journey with his wife.

It was late spring. There was a gentle wind in the trees and a light rain fell.

The road to Chiang-chou took Ch'en and his wife close to his home, so they stopped at his mother's house. Ch'en said to his mother, 'You wanted me to take the examination, and look at all the good luck that has come from it. I would like to thank you and to ask you to come with us.'

His mother happily agreed and after travelling for some days, the three arrived at the Hotel of Ten Thousand Flowers. But here the mother suddenly became ill and asked to rest.

Next day, a man arrived with a gold-coloured fish for sale and young Ch'en bought it for his mother. Suddenly, he noticed that the fish's eyes were strange. 'This is not an ordinary creature,' he said. He asked where it was caught and then returned it to the river in the same place.

'You were right to put the fish back in the river,' said his mother when he told her about the fish's eyes. Then she said, 'Leave me here with some of the luggage and I shall follow when the days are cooler.'

When Ch'en, his wife and servants arrived at the same river, they were met by two boatmen who Ch'en had harmed in an earlier life. They stared at his young wife, who was very beautiful. Then they took the boat to a lonely place and killed first the servants and then Ch'en himself. The young woman tried to throw herself into the river, but they stopped her.

One of the murderers, whose name was Liu, put on the Governor's clothes, took the official papers and left for Chiang-chou with Mrs Ch'en.

Liu left the boat with the other boatman, Li, who threw the bodies into the river. The bodies of the servants could be seen on the river, but Ch'en's body went straight to the bottom. A servant of the Dragon King saw it there and went to the palace to tell the Dragon King himself. The Dragon King asked to see it.

When Ch'en's body was brought to him, he recognised this man. In the body of a gold-coloured fish, the Dragon King had been saved by him only a few days before. In return for Ch'en's kindness, the Dragon King sent his servant to the place where the souls of the newly dead go. The servant returned with Ch'en's soul and Ch'en woke from the dead.

When he had heard Ch'en's story, the Dragon King said, 'You certainly helped me. So I shall now give you back your life. I want you to work in my Water Office.'

While this was happening, Mrs Ch'en was so unhappy with Liu that she could not eat or sleep. But because she was going to have her husband's child, she thought it was best to follow this terrible man quietly. After a long journey they reached Chiang-chou, where Liu the boatman became the new governor.

Time passed and Mrs Ch'en gave birth to a son. At the same time a mysterious voice whispered in her ear, 'Listen to what I am telling you. This child will be famous around the world. But you must protect him from Liu, who will certainly try to harm him. Your husband is safe with the Dragon King and one day you will all be together again and your enemies will be punished.' Then there was silence. Mrs Ch'en held her son in her arms, but she could think of no other way to protect him.

And as the voice had said, when Liu returned he ordered the death of the child. But the unhappy mother wanted more time with her son. 'I will put him in the river tomorrow,' she promised Liu. 'Perhaps,' she thought, 'a kind god will save him.'

She bit her finger and, with her blood, wrote a letter giving the names of the child's parents. Then, so that she would know her child again, she bit off the top of the little toe of his left foot. When morning came, she tied the baby into one of her shirts and went quietly down to the river with him.

As she stood at the water's edge, a large piece of wood came down the river. Quickly, she tied the shirt with the baby in it to the wood and put the letter she had written in the shirt. Then she pushed the wood to the centre of the river and walked back, crying every step of the way.

The piece of wood with the baby on it was carried at last to the **Temple** of the Golden Mountain. The **Holy Master**, hearing the sound of a baby crying, went to the river and found the strange boat. He read the letter about the child's father, and immediately gave the child the name of River Wood. Then he asked some farmers to look after him.

temple /ˈtempəl/ (n) a place where people of some religions go to speak to their gods or god
holy /ˈhəʊli/ (adj) serving God and religion
master /ˈmɑːstə/ (n) a person who has the power of control

Seventeen years later, the young man had been given the new name of Hsüan Tsang and had been made a priest in the Holy Master's temple. One day an old and stupid priest cried out, 'Who do you think you are? No one even knows your real name!' He was jealous of the young man's wisdom.

The unhappy boy ran to the Holy Master. 'Can there be,' he asked, 'a man without a father or mother?'

From a hiding-place in his room, the Holy Master took down a small box containing the blood-letter and the shirt. Soon Hsüan Tsang knew the whole story and the terrible wrong done to his parents. He wanted to kill his father's murderer.

'If you must go,' said the Holy Master, 'take these things with you. Travel as a poor priest, go to Chiang-chou and demand to see your mother.'

That same night, his mother dreamed of a moon behind the clouds. When the clouds moved, she saw a full moon, and then she thought of her son. 'He must be seventeen by now. Perhaps Heaven will bring us together again.'

Suddenly, she heard a priest asking for money at the gate and went out to him. When she heard his place of birth, the Golden Mountain, she looked at him closely and said, 'Little priest, you are very like my husband. Who were your parents?'

'A wrong was done to my parents,' was the answer. 'My Holy Master told me to come here and find my mother. My father's name is Ch'en, but my holy name is Hsüan Tsang.' Then he took from the box the blood-letter and the shirt. She recognised them at once and she put her arms around him.

'Leave me, leave me!' she cried. 'If Liu finds you, he will kill you. Go now, as fast as lightning! But tomorrow I will say that I have promised a hundred pairs of shoes to the poor and I must journey to the temple to offer this present to the Gods. There we can talk.'

True to her promise, within five days a hundred pairs of shoes were put on a boat and, with some servants, she made the journey to the Golden Mountain. All the priests came out to welcome the visitor, but when she had **prayed** she asked them to leave.

Then, on her knees in front of Hsüan Tsang, she took off the shoe and sock from his left foot. As she expected, the top of his left toe was missing.

Again the mother and son put their arms around each other, and she thanked the Holy Master for his great kindness. Then she gave Hsüan Tsang a ring to take to the Hotel of Ten Thousand Flowers, where his grandmother had been left behind.

'Here, also, is a letter to my father in the capital,' she said. 'Tell him to ask the

pray /preɪ/ (v) to speak, often silently, to a god. Your words are *prayers*.

Emperor to send horses and men to kill Liu and save me. Now I dare not stay any longer, but must return home.'

Hsüan Tsang went to the Hotel of Ten Thousand Flowers and asked about his grandmother. The owner of the hotel told him, 'The lady was here for several years. But she went blind and now, asking people in the streets for money, she lives in a box.'

Hsüan Tsang finally found his poor grandmother, who cried, 'Oh! I thought my son had forgotten me! And now Heaven has sent a grandson to find me.'

After paying her bills and leaving her in a comfortable room at the hotel, Hsüan Tsang rushed back to the capital and to the house of Minister Yin. But they refused to let him in. 'No one in our family is a priest,' he was told.

'Last night I dreamed about my daughter,' said the wife. 'Perhaps he has a message from her.'

Hsüan Tsang bowed to them and took out the letter that his mother had written. The minister cried, 'Wife! This is our grandchild. Ch'en has been killed and our daughter has been forced to live with the murderer. I will ask the Emperor for soldiers to kill that man.'

The Emperor was wild with anger and sent an army of sixty thousand men to Chiang-chou. They easily found Liu and took him away to cut his head off.

Now Yin sent for his daughter. She did not wish to see her father because she was ashamed. Had she not lived as the wife of her husband's murderer? But Yin told her that it was not her fault. He put his arms around her and around his grandson and kept them in his arms for a long, long time.

By now, the soldiers had found the other boatman, Li, and had cut his head off too. And where he had killed Ch'en, Li's body was cut open. His heart was offered to the soul of the man he had killed.

The Dragon King heard of this and he sent a message to Ch'en. 'Congratulations! Your wife and her father and your child are all by the river, offering the heart of the man who killed you. I will now return your soul to you and let you go.'

Mrs Ch'en wanted to throw herself into the river where her husband had died, but suddenly a body came up from the bottom of the river. Mrs Ch'en recognised it as her husband's body and cried and screamed.

The hands moved, and then the legs, and then the whole body, until Ch'en himself climbed out of the water. He looked at them in great surprise and said, 'What are you all doing here?'

A great banquet was ordered and next day they all left for home. On the way, they called at the Hotel of Ten Thousand Flowers for the grandmother and took her back to the capital.

At last Ch'en became a government advisor. His son, Hsüan Tsang, went back to his work as a priest at the Temple of the Golden Mountain. But when the Emperor died, priests all over China were asked to choose the holiest priest, and they chose Hsüan Tsang.

At this time, the search was still continuing for a priest holy enough to fetch the Scriptures from India. The Goddess Kuan-yin, realising that the holiest priest was River Wood, said to herself, 'No one could be a better man than him.'

In the great city of Ch'ang-an, the new Emperor asked Hsüan Tsang to go to India and fetch the Scriptures. When Hsüan Tsang agreed to go, the Emperor said, 'If you dare to go on a journey as long as this, with all its dangers, I will make you here and now the brother of my soul.' Then he bowed four times.

'If I do not reach India and do not bring the Scriptures back to China, I must be sent to Hell,' the young priest replied.

The Emperor called for wine and said, 'I suggest that you take the name of the Scriptures in India – Tripitaka. What do you think?'

Hsüan Tsang accepted the name and from that day he was called Tripitaka.

It was three days before the full moon when Tripitaka left the gates of Ch'ang-an. After a day or two of hard riding, he reached the Temple of the Low Cloud. There the Holy Master and almost five hundred priests discussed his journey and its terrible dangers and difficulties. Tripitaka pointed in silence to his heart.

'It is only the heart that can win against difficulties. I have made my promise and I cannot go back until I have reached India, seen Buddha and got the Scriptures.'

Next morning, Tripitaka got up early. A bright moon was shining on the snow on the ground as he left. Almost immediately, he lost his way, and suddenly the ground moved under his horse. The horse and rider fell into a deep hole.

'Take him! Take him!'

Looking up, Tripitaka saw a crowd of ugly creatures looking down at him. They pulled him out of the hole. Their leader was an ugly Demon King, who gave orders to eat him.

But two dark ugly creatures arrived as guests, and two other men were brought out as a meal for them. The ugly creatures ate like wild animals, their teeth pulling at the men until they had completely eaten them. Watching this, Tripitaka was almost dead with fear.

But then all the ugly creatures went to sleep. Tripitaka was losing all hope of escape when suddenly an old man appeared. He blew in Tripitaka's face and asked him if the horse belonged to him. Tripitaka saw to his surprise that his horse was not harmed. He asked what this place was and who the ugly creatures were. He was told it was a mountain full of demons and animal-spirits.

'They did not eat you because your soul was too good,' said the old man. 'It was your soul that saved you. Follow me and I will show you the way out of here.'

The old man led him out of that place; then, as Tripitaka turned to thank him, the old man flew up into the sky on a great white bird. A piece of paper blew down, and on it was written, 'I was sent by the Gods to protect you on your journey. Remember, the Gods will be watching you.'

Tripitaka could only bow low in thanks before he began his journey again. After half a day he found himself in difficult mountain country, moving forward slowly over sharp rocks. In front of him, two **tigers** waited. Realising the danger, he looked behind him and there he saw an insect that could kill him. On his right stood a wild animal that he had never seen before. His frightened horse went down on its knees.

As the terrible creatures all started attacking him at once, a man appeared with a sword. He took Tripitaka from his horse.

'I am a hunter who these animals know and fear. You and I are from the same country and you and your horse can rest at my house until tomorrow.'

On the way to his house the hunter killed a tiger, saying, 'This is luck! Enough meat to last you for days!'

tiger /ˈtaɪgə/ (n) a very dangerous big yellow and black Asian wild cat

Arriving at a mountain farm, Tripitaka was presented to the hunter's mother, who invited him to stay overnight. But when the cooked tiger was put in front of him he had to say that, as a priest, he did not eat meat. He was given rice and salad instead. Then, putting his hands together, he said a prayer.

The hunter was surprised. 'You priests are certainly strange,' he said. 'You cannot even eat without a prayer.'

After dinner the hunter led his guest to a little house full of animal skins. Tripitaka did not like that very much, so his host took him instead to a field of red and gold flowers. There, animals ran to him when he called.

Tripitaka had been asked by the hunter's mother to say prayers for her dead husband. So scriptures were read and prayers were said all through the next day until evening.

That night everyone in the family dreamed the same dream: the hunter's father had been allowed to leave the Lower World and was born again as the child of a rich landowner. This, they were sure, was a result of Tripitaka's prayers and they all thanked him. They wanted to give him presents of silver, but he refused the presents and left on his journey, with the hunter as his guide.

At the Mountain Between Two Countries, which was steep and rocky, the hunter climbed quickly but Tripitaka was very tired.

'This country to the East,' said the hunter, 'is our land of T'ang, and to the West is the country of the Tartars. I cannot go into their country, so you must continue alone.'

Feeling a great fear and hopelessness, Tripitaka held the hunter's arm. Suddenly, from under the mountain, a voice cried, again and again, 'The Master has come.'

'Who is that?' Tripitaka asked, fearfully.

'It is the voice of the old monkey calling from his stone box under the mountain. The story is that long ago, when the mountain was called the Mountain of Metal, Wood, Water, Fire and Earth, a magic monkey was put in a stone box by angry gods. He is certainly still alive. You need not be afraid. We will go down and have a look.'

As the hunter had said, there was a stone box with a hole in it, and through the opening they could see the head of a monkey.

'Master! Master! Free me from here and I will protect you on your journey to the West!'

The hunter said, 'First, we want to know more about you.'

'I will not tell you anything,' said Monkey. 'I wish to speak to the priest.'

'What do you want to say to me?' asked Tripitaka.

'Were you sent by the Emperor of T'ang to fetch the Scriptures from India?'

'I was.'

'I am the Monkey King and five hundred years ago I made trouble, so Buddha put me in this stone box. The Goddess Kuan-yin has visited me. She said that if I protect the pilgrim on his way to India I will be forgiven and freed. So let me be your follower.'

'But how can I get you out of this stone box?'

'If you make a wish, Master, I will be out,' said Monkey. 'Go to the top of the mountain and there you will see a rock with letters of gold written by Buddha himself. Lift the rock and I will be free.'

'How can we believe him?' the hunter whispered to Tripitaka.

'It is true! It is true!' screamed Monkey, from inside his box.

Tripitaka and the hunter climbed up again to the top of the mountain, and there they saw golden light pouring from a rock which had gold writing on it.

Tripitaka went down on his knees and said, 'If this is the wish of the Gods, I will take this Monkey with me to India. Take away this rock and free him.'

A warm and sweet-smelling wind blew across the mountain and lifted the rock and Buddha's writing up into the air. Tripitaka and the hunter returned to Monkey.

'You can come out,' they said. With a great noise of breaking stone, Monkey came out of the stone box and bowed in front of Tripitaka. He cried, 'Master, I am out,' and then he began to prepare Tripitaka's horse for the journey.

Tripitaka thanked the hunter for his kindness and he and Monkey continued their journey.

When Tripitaka and Monkey left the mountain, a tiger appeared in front of them, showing its teeth. Monkey seemed very happy. 'He has come to give me his coat,' he said.

He took a needle from behind his ear and the needle was immediately transformed into a cudgel. 'It is five hundred years since I last used this weapon,' he cried.

Look at Monkey! He walks forward bravely, down comes the cudgel, and the tiger falls dead.

'Sit down,' said Monkey to Tripitaka, 'while I take his coat.'

Dear Monkey! He took a single hair from his own tail, blew on it, and said some magic words. The hair became a sharp little knife, and with this knife he cut off the tiger's skin. 'Now we can leave this place,' he said. 'When we reach the next house, I will make a fine coat from the skin.'

Monkey then explained the magic of his cudgel, which was not only for killing tigers and dragons, but also for making rivers go backwards or starting storms on the sea. But then he saw a house in some trees, where they could spend the night.

He got down from his horse and cried, 'Open the door!'

A very old man, angry at the rude command, began to push open the door. But seeing Monkey carrying a tiger skin and looking like a demon, he became very frightened. Then he saw that Monkey was with a priest and he was told that Monkey was the priest's follower. Suddenly, he recognised Monkey.

'You are the Stone Monkey in the stone box,' said the old man in great surprise. 'How did you get out?'

Monkey told his story and then was asked his age.

'First, how old are *you*?' asked Monkey.

'One hundred and thirty.'

'You are young enough to be my great-great-grandson,' said Monkey. 'I was under that mountain for five hundred years.'

'True,' said the old man. 'And when I was a boy, there was grass on your head and dirt on your face.'

'Yes!' said Monkey. 'I do not wish to make trouble, but it is five hundred years since I last washed. Could you let us have a little hot water?'

When they had both washed, Monkey took Tripitaka's white shirt, made himself a tiger-skin coat and asked, 'How do I look in these clothes?'

'Fine!' said Tripitaka. 'You really look like a pilgrim!' And he let Monkey keep the shirt.

Many days later, the two travellers were attacked by six men with swords. The men demanded their horses and everything they had with them.

'You are just thieves!' cried Monkey. 'If you give me one seventh of everything you have ever stolen, I will let you live.'

Angrily, they all hit Monkey on the head, again and again.

Monkey said, 'Let me know when you are tired and I will take out my needle.'

Of course the needle from behind Monkey's ear transformed itself into a cudgel, and soon he had killed all six of them. He returned, crying, 'Master, we can start now. I have killed them all.'

'You should *never* kill,' said Tripitaka, sadly.

'But I had to! They were going to kill *you*!'

'It is better for a priest to die than to kill others.'

'Well, I can tell you that I have killed quite a lot of people. And I am still the great Monkey King!' answered Monkey.

'Your bad behaviour in Heaven caused you to live in a stone box for five hundred years,' said Tripitaka. 'If you hope to come with me to India, you will need to change your ways.'

Monkey was very angry that Tripitaka had spoken to him like that. 'Master,' he shouted, 'I am leaving.'

Tripitaka said nothing, so Monkey leapt up, ran away and was soon out of Tripitaka's sight.

Tripitaka thought, 'It is no use trying to teach people who are like that.' So, putting all the luggage on the horse's back, he left alone and on foot.

The young priest had not gone far when he met an old woman carrying a cap. She asked him why he was travelling alone without a follower to help him.

'I had a follower, but he behaved badly. When I told him that, he ran away.'

'That is unfortunate,' she said. 'This cap belonged to my son, who died. I can gladly give it your follower if he would like it.'

'He ran away to the East,' said Tripitaka.

'Then he will certainly go to my house and I shall send him back. If you want him to return, you will need a **spell**.' She told him the words. 'You must make him wear this cap. When he disobeys, say the words of the spell and he will give you no more trouble.'

The old woman transformed herself into a golden light and disappeared towards the East. Tripitaka knew then that she was really the Goddess Kuan-yin.

Monkey had jumped on to a cloud and was returning to his cave in the Mountain of Flowers and Fruit. On the way, he decided to drink tea with the Dragon King. When Monkey had told his story, the Dragon King told him about the value of patience.

'Monkey King, it is necessary to control yourself if you do not want to spoil all your chances.'

Monkey thought about that and then jumped up. 'Don't say another word!'

spell /spel/ (n) magic words that have power over people

he said. 'I will return to my Master at once.'

'Master,' said Monkey, when he found Tripitaka sitting sadly by the side of the road, 'what are you doing, still sitting here?'

'Waiting for you,' he answered. 'I could not continue alone.'

'I only went to drink tea with the Dragon King,' said Monkey.

'If that is true, you should think about *my* thirst and *my* hunger too.'

Monkey went to their luggage to look for food and found the gift of the cap.

'If a person wears that cap,' said Tripitaka, 'they can recite the Scriptures without learning them first.'

'Let me put it on!' cried Monkey.

'Yes, put it on.'

As Monkey put it on, Tripitaka pretended to eat some dried fruit, but he was really reciting the magic spell.

'My head is hurting!' screamed Monkey.

Monkey fell on the ground, trying to take the cap off, but a metal ring inside the cap was getting tighter and tighter. Tripitaka stopped reciting the spell because he was afraid that Monkey would break the metal ring.

The pain in Monkey's head disappeared, but the cap was still tightly there.

'You have put a spell on me,' cried Monkey.

'Yes,' said Tripitaka. 'It is called the Scripture of the Tight Cap. Will you make trouble again?'

'Never! I promise,' answered Monkey, but in his heart he was very angry. He ran at Tripitaka with his cudgel.

Quickly, the priest again recited the words of the spell, and Monkey fell to the ground screaming. The cudgel dropped from his hand.

'Were you going to hit me?' Tripitaka asked.

'Hit you? I dare not!' cried Monkey.

Tripitaka stopped reciting because he did not like to see Monkey suffering such terrible pain.

'Who taught you this trick?' Monkey asked when the pain stopped.

'An old woman who I met recently.'

'Then it was the Goddess Kuan-yin. I will go to the Southern Ocean and hit her with my cudgel!'

'As she taught me this spell, she can surely use it herself,' said Tripitaka.

Monkey sat up, holding his head, which still hurt him. 'I am very sorry,' he said. 'I will travel to India and never leave you. I will protect you until the end.'

Unable to defend himself, Monkey put the luggage together, and they started off again towards the West.

3.1 Were you right?

1 Look at your answers to Activity 2.4. Match the pictures with the names.

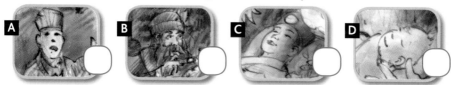

1 Ch'en O, the father of the pilgrim.

2 Tripitaka, the pilgrim, whose name was Hsŭan Tsang.

3 River Wood, the pilgrim, soon after his birth.

4 The hunter who helps the pilgrim to free Monkey.

2 Now write the correct names in these sentences.

a .... is killed by boatmen, but saved by the Dragon King.

b Liu becomes the new governor and lives with ....'s wife.

c She ties her son to a piece of wood and puts him in the river. When he is found, he is given the name ....

d When the child is seventeen, he becomes a priest in the Holy Master's temple and is given the new name ....

e The Goddess Kuan-yin wants him to fetch the Scriptures. After he accepts, the Emperor gives him the name ....

3.2 What more did you learn?

Read about Tripitaka's journey and circle the best words in *italics*.

1 Tripitaka's *soul / horse* saves him from demons.

2 Tripitaka is then attacked by dangerous *insects / tigers*.

3 Tripitaka's prayers give new life to a hunter's *father / son*.

4 Tripitaka's *prayers / actions* save Monkey from his stone box.

5 Monkey transforms a needle into a *sword / cudgel* and a hair into a *stick / knife*.

6 Kuan-yin gives Tripitaka a cap and a *coat / spell* to control Monkey.

3.3 **Language in use**

Read the sentences in the box.
Then re-write these sentences
using passive verb forms.

> The winner of first place in the examination **was led** through the streets.
>
> Ch'en and the minister's daughter **were married**.

1   They made Ch'en Governor of Chiang-chou.

      Ch'en was made Governor of Chiang-chou

2   Two boatmen met Ch'en, his wife and two servants.

      ....

3   A servant brought Ch'en's body to the Dragon King.

      ....

4   Servants put a hundred pairs of shoes on a boat.

      ....

5   They offered Li's heart to the soul of the man he had killed.

      ....

3.4 **What happens next?**

Read the title of Chapter 3 and the
sentences in *italics* below it. Then
look at the pictures in this chapter.
What do you think happens to
Tripitaka's horse and followers?
Discuss these questions.

1   What do you know about the horse?

2   How will Kuan-yin help Tripitaka and his followers?

3   What special weapons will Monkey use?

4   What has Kuan-yin promised Pigsy?

5   What will the nine heads around Sandy Priest's neck do for the travellers?

CHAPTER 3

Tripitaka Finds New Followers

With her magic breath she shouted 'Change!' She transformed the Dragon into the horse that he had just eaten.

It was the middle of winter and a cold wind was blowing from the North. There was ice everywhere and deep snow was lying on the ground. But the brave priest, his follower and the white horse continued their journey across the mountains.

They were looking down at a river when suddenly a dragon appeared in it and then climbed slowly out of the water. While Monkey and Tripitaka ran and hid, the Dragon, moving along at speed and without stopping, opened its mouth and ate the horse.

Monkey left Tripitaka sitting on a rock and went back to get the horse and luggage, but he could not find the horse. He took the luggage to the place where he had left Tripitaka.

'The Dragon is gone,' said Monkey, 'and the horse is too. It probably ran away because it was frightened.'

'How are we going to find it?' asked Tripitaka.

'Wait here and I will have a look,' said Monkey.

Monkey leapt into the sky and looked for it with his bright red eyes.

'I cannot see it anywhere,' he told Tripitaka. 'I think the Dragon ate it.'

'How can I travel if it has been eaten? It is much too far to walk,' cried Tripitaka. Poor Tripitaka was so sad that he could not stop crying.

Monkey, who hated that kind of attitude, shouted at Tripitaka, 'You look like a fool, sitting there crying! Wait there while I go after the Dragon.'

'You cannot do anything to the Dragon if he is in the water,' said the young priest, still crying. 'And next time he will eat *me*.'

'You are hopeless! Hopeless!' shouted Monkey, angrier than ever. 'Do you want to sit there staring at the luggage for ever?'

He was still shouting angrily when the voices of Gods were heard in the sky. 'Monkey, don't be angry. Priest, don't cry. We are here to protect you,' they said.

'Then you had better stay here and look after the Master,' said Monkey. 'I am going to find that horse! Don't worry about me!'

Tripitaka, feeling better, asked Monkey to be careful.

Dear Monkey! He pulled his tiger-skin coat around his body, picked up his cudgel and walked down to the river.

'You demon fish, return my horse to me,' he called into the water.

The Dragon leapt out of the river. 'Who is making all that noise?' it shouted, angrily.

'Come and fight,' shouted Monkey, as he waved his cudgel. 'And give me back my horse!'

Monkey hit the Dragon's head with his cudgel. The Dragon came forwards with his mouth wide open. It was a long and brave fight. They fought backwards and forwards, round and round, and up and down until the Dragon began to feel weak. With a quick turn of his long tail, he disappeared back into the river. Monkey shouted for him to come back and fight, but the Dragon did not listen. Monkey decided to go back and tell Tripitaka.

When Monkey returned, Tripitaka said something that Monkey did not like. 'The other day, after you fought the tiger, you said you could also kill dragons. I do not understand why you are having such difficulties with this dragon.'

'Not another word!' he cried. 'I will soon show you who is master!'

Annoyed, Monkey went back to the river and used his magic to make a storm. The Dragon leapt up and shouted, 'What sort of creature are you? Where do you come from?'

'That is not your business – just return my horse!'

'How can I? Your horse is inside me. And if I do not, what will you do to me?'

'Look at this cudgel,' said Monkey. 'If you do not give me back the horse, you will pay for it with your life.'

Again they fought, and then the Dragon transformed himself into an insect and disappeared into the long grass. Beating the grass with his cudgel, Monkey danced around wildly, trying to find him. But it was impossible. So Monkey returned to Tripitaka, who was feeling quite sorry for himself.

'I will be dead from cold or hunger before we get across this river,' said Tripitaka.

Monkey danced and jumped and leapt in anger, but finally he had to ask the Goddess Kuan-yin for help. When he saw her, he became angry again.

'You told me to look after this priest,' shouted Monkey. 'So why did you give him a cap that I cannot take off my head? It gives me terrible pains when he says the words of the spell!'

The Goddess laughed. 'Because you are so full of tricks, there is no other way to control you.'

'But what about this dragon? That is your work too. Why did you let him eat my Master's horse? You should be ashamed of yourself!'

'That dragon,' said the Goddess Kuan-yin, 'behaved badly in Heaven. If he carries the priest of the Emperor T'ang on his journey to India, he will be forgiven and he knows this. No ordinary Chinese horse could possibly do it. I cannot understand why he ate the horse. I will go with you and find out.'

She got down from her seat inside her cave and rode on a magic light to find the Dragon. When the Dragon saw Kuan-yin, he changed into a human.

'Did you know that this is Tripitaka's follower?' asked Kuan-yin.

'How could I? I asked him what kind of creature he was and he shouted at me, "That is not your business." I ate his horse because I was hungry. He never said anything about looking for Scriptures. He never once used the word "T'ang".'

'Monkey is fonder of showing others his own powers than explaining anything,' said Kuan-yin. 'But in future, if anyone questions him, he must say that he is looking for Scriptures. Then there will be no more trouble.'

The Goddess went to the Dragon and put some drops of sweet water on him. Then with her magic breath she shouted 'Change!' She transformed the Dragon into the horse that he had just eaten. She told the Dragon to change his bad behaviour and to promise never to go back to his old ways.

'If you keep this promise, you will be given a golden body,' she told him, 'and you will be given wisdom.'

The Dragon said, 'Thank you. I will keep this promise.'

Then the Goddess turned to go, but Monkey held her arm saying, 'That is not good enough! How can I help a priest to travel over these mountains with only a horse? I cannot continue this journey.'

'That is strange,' said the Goddess. 'You always used to be brave, if nothing else. But there is one more power I can give you.'

She took three leaves from a tree and dropped them on Monkey's back, where they immediately became magic hairs.

'These,' she said, 'will get you out of any trouble.'

Monkey thanked her. Then he took the horse and led him to Tripitaka.

'This horse is in much better condition than the old one. How did you manage to find it?' asked Tripitaka.

Monkey answered, 'Kuan-yin changed the Dragon into the horse that he had eaten.'

Tripitaka wanted to say 'thank you' to Kuan-yin, but Monkey said that she was already far away. So Tripitaka bowed towards the South. Then he helped Monkey to prepare their luggage.

'We still need a boat to cross this river,' said the priest.

'Just sit on the horse and he will carry you across,' Monkey replied.

But then an old fisherman in a strange boat appeared. Monkey waved to him. 'We have come from the East to fetch scriptures. My Master does not know how to get across the river. Could you take him?'

The old fisherman took them all across the river, without asking for payment.

'Do you know who that fisherman was?' said Monkey. 'He is the God of the River and he did not help us in our fight against the Dragon. He knew he had done wrong. That is why he did not take any money.'

Tripitaka did not know how true that story was. But he sat on the horse and followed Monkey along the road to the West.

One evening they saw a group of houses in the far distance.

'Let me go and see if it is a farm and if it seems lucky or unlucky,' said Monkey.

A young man in a blue jacket came out of the farm and tried to walk past Monkey without a word. But Monkey held his arm tightly while the young man tried to escape.

'Now, you must not be angry,' laughed Monkey, holding him even tighter. 'We only want to know the name of this place.'

The young man, seeing that he could not get away from Monkey, answered, 'The place is called Kao Farm and I am Kao Ts'ai. Old Mr Kao has a daughter of twenty who is unmarried. Three years ago, a creature took her and has lived with her here as his wife. Six months ago the creature locked her in his little house, and none of the family has seen her since then. I am going to find someone with strong enough magic to fight this creature.'

'This is your lucky day,' said Monkey. 'Here I am, and I can help you. Come, lead us to the master of the house.'

'Your words are true, I hope,' said the young man. 'You will get me into great trouble if you fail.'

'I promise,' said Monkey. 'Now, take us in.'

Seeing the young man returning, old Mr Kao shouted, 'You fool!' But he quickly became more polite when he saw the young priest. Seeing Monkey, though, he said, 'It is surely bad enough to have a dirty creature living with my daughter. Now another ugly creature has come to visit me.'

'You have lived a long time but have learned very little wisdom,' said Monkey. 'You should not judge people only by appearances. But I shall return your daughter to you.'

'I do not understand. I thought you wanted a bed for the night.'

'Yes, we do,' said Monkey. 'But I am also happy to kill any dirty creatures for you, for something to do.'

'We have three daughters. Our hope was that the youngest would marry a farmer and work this farm. Well, about three years ago, a nice-looking young man came here and said his name was Pig. He seemed the right man for our daughter and at first he worked hard on the farm. But then he started to change: his nose became longer, his ears became bigger, he ate more and more. Finally, he turned into a pig. But that was not all. He could bring magic winds, he could disappear and then appear again, he could make stones fly through the air. And now he keeps our daughter, Blue Flower, in his little house, and for six months we have not known if she is alive or dead.'

'Have no fear,' said Monkey. 'I shall catch him tonight and return your daughter to you.'

'But do you need weapons?'

'I have my weapon already,' said Monkey, taking his needle from behind his ear and changing it into an iron cudgel. 'I need only a nice old person to sit with my Master and talk to him. And now I will leave you!'

Old Mr Kao led Monkey to the little house and Monkey broke the door with one blow of his hand. Inside it was dark as the old man called, 'Number three daughter!'

'Father, I am here.'

Monkey looked hard with his red eyes and saw a sad sight. The daughter's face was unwashed, her hair was full of dirt and her lips were pale. She walked slowly forwards and fell, crying, into her father's arms.

'Don't make that noise. But where is the creature?' asked Monkey.

'I do not know,' said the unhappy girl. 'He goes out early in the morning and does not come back until late at night.'

'Take your daughter back to the house and stay with her,' said Monkey to Mr Kao. 'I shall wait here and end your troubles.'

When the girl and her father had gone, Monkey transformed himself into a girl who looked like Blue Flower. Then he waited. Soon stones came flying through the air and there in front of him stood a terrible creature. He had short hairs on his dark skin, a long nose and enormous ears. He wore a green jacket and had a spotted handkerchief tied round his head.

Dear Monkey! He did not say hello to the creature. He lay on the bed making noises like a person who is ill. When the creature tried to kiss him, he pushed it hard across the room.

'Why are you angry with me?' asked the creature.

'I am not angry. Get into bed.'

The creature undressed in the dark, but could not find his wife in the bed. Then he heard her crying on the far side of the room.

'Oh, I am so unhappy!'

'What are you complaining about?' asked the creature. 'Have I not kept my promises to you? I have worked on the farm, built walls and dug new fields. You have all the food and clothes that you need.'

'That is not the problem,' said Monkey in Blue Flower's voice. 'Today my parents came and shouted through the wall that you are ugly. And nobody knows anything about you or who you are.'

'There is no mystery about who I am. Because I look a little like a pig, I am called Pigsy. Next time they ask, just tell them that.'

'They are looking for a priest to send you away,' said Monkey. 'In fact, old Mr Kao has called the great Monkey King himself to help.'

'If that is true, I am leaving this minute,' cried the creature. 'That Monkey is very powerful!' And getting dressed quickly, he opened the door to leave.

With a magic spell, Monkey transformed himself back again.

'Look around,' he cried, 'and you will see that I am Monkey.'

When Pigsy turned and saw Monkey, with his sharp little teeth and big smile, his red eyes, flat head and hairy face, he ran like the wind back to his cave.

Monkey cried after him, 'Where are you going? If you go up to Heaven, I will follow you. And if you go down to the deepest part of Hell, I will follow you there too.'

Monkey followed the creature to his cave and it came out waving a fork. They fought together all night, but at last the creature leapt back into the cave and locked the door. Monkey now saw the name of the cave on a rock: it was Cloud-Ladder Cave.

'I had better return to my Master now, because he might want something,' Monkey thought. 'I can always return and catch this creature.' And leaping from one cloud to another, he was soon back at the farm.

No one had slept all night, waiting for Monkey's return. Tripitaka was sitting with the old man when Monkey arrived.

'Master, here I am,' he said.

'Did you have to go a long way to catch the creature?' asked Tripitaka.

'That is no ordinary creature. He used to live in Heaven, where he was in charge of water-spirits. But he did wrong and he was sent down to Earth as a pig-like creature. He still has all his magic powers. I chased him to his mountain cave, where he fetched a large fork and we fought all night. As the sun came up, he gave up the fight and locked himself in his cave. I was going to beat down the door, but I knew it was going to take some time. I thought Master might be getting anxious so I wanted to report back here.'

'Monkey King,' said old Mr Kao, 'you have driven him away, but he is certain to come back. If you can get him for us, you can have half of all that is ours.'

'I think you worry too much about him. He knows that he eats a lot. But he has also done a lot of work around here. He feels that his work easily pays for the cost of feeding him. He is a god who has been sent to Earth as a punishment. It seems that he has done no harm to your daughter,' said Monkey.

'It is true,' said old Mr Kao, 'that he has done her no harm. But it is very bad for our family name. Everywhere I go, I hear, "Mr Kao has taken a dirty creature for his daughter's husband." What can I say to that?'

'Monkey,' said Tripitaka, 'do you not think that you should return? Have one more fight with him and see if you can find a way to end this difficult situation.'

'Don't worry. I was only having a little game with him. This time I will catch him and bring him back here. Look after my Master until I get back!' Monkey said to Mr Kao.

Monkey disappeared into the clouds and soon arrived at the cave. This time, Pigsy was asleep in his cave when Monkey broke the door in pieces. Angrily, Pigsy jumped out of bed and took up his fork again.

'You dirty rat! What do you think you are doing? It is a crime to break down someone else's door!' shouted Pigsy. 'I remember you now …' he said, looking more closely at Monkey. 'You once lived in a cave behind a Water Curtain. How did you get here?'

'I am a priest now. I am going with a Chinese pilgrim called Tripitaka to fetch scriptures from India.'

The fork fell from Pigsy's hand. 'Where is the pilgrim?' he said. 'Take me to him.'

'Why do *you* want to see him?' asked Monkey.

'The Goddess Kuan-yin put me here to prepare myself for the arrival of a pilgrim who I must follow. After doing this, I will receive wisdom. I have been waiting for this pilgrim for years. Why did you not tell me that you are his follower? Why did you prefer to fight with me?'

'I am not so sure that your story is true. If you really want to follow my Master to India, you must promise that this story is true. Then I will take you to him.'

Pigsy threw himself down on his knees and bowed repeatedly. 'I promise holy Buddha, this is true – every word. If it is not true, let the judges in Heaven cut me into ten thousand pieces.'

'I believe you,' said Monkey, 'but give me your fork.' Then Monkey took a hair, blew on it with his magic breath, and changed it into a long thick string. He tied Pigsy's hands behind his back, took him by the ear and pulled him along with him.

When Monkey arrived at Mr Kao's farm with Pigsy, everyone was very happy. After hearing Pigsy's story, Tripitaka told Monkey to untie him. Tripitaka said some prayers and then they sat down and ate supper together.

The next day, Tripitaka sat on the white horse that had been a dragon. Pigsy carried the luggage and Monkey carried his cudgel, as they all left for the West.

At last they came to a flat country. Summer had passed and autumn had come, and now in front of them was a great, wild river.

Monkey leapt into the air and looked far down into the water.

'Master,' he reported, 'this will not be easy. For me, it will not be difficult because I can jump across in one leap, but for you it will be impossible. When I looked down, I saw that this river is twelve thousand kilometres across.'

Tripitaka was very unhappy but, looking down, he saw a rock with some writing which said *River of Sands*. Under that, in small letters, were the words:

In the River of Sands, twelve thousand wide,
In Dead Waters, fifteen thousand deep,
Nothing will stay on the water –
Even the lightest flower goes straight to the bottom.

As they looked, a terrible creature came towards them through the water. His eyes were like bright lights, and around his neck were nine heads. He rushed straight at the pilgrims.

Monkey pushed Tripitaka to a safe place while Pigsy attacked the creature with his fork. The creature fought hard and the fight was a good one. Monkey was impatient to join in and at last, with a wild scream, he leapt at the creature. As he brought his cudgel down on its head, it disappeared into the water.

Pigsy was very angry. 'Brother, who asked you to fight my fight? That creature was just getting tired and I had almost finished him. You have spoilt everything.'

'I am sorry,' laughed Monkey. 'But I could not stand and watch. I have not used my cudgel for months and I got so excited that I could not stop myself. I wanted to join the fun.'

So, hand in hand, they returned to Tripitaka.

'It will be your turn next time,' promised Pigsy.

'Thank you, but I am really not at my best in water,' said Monkey. 'I am happier in the clouds and I have enough tricks on land. If you can make this creature leave the river, I will come and help you.'

Pigsy went into the river and discovered that he had not lost his water-magic. He soon found the creature at the bottom of the river.

'You ugly pig,' the creature shouted. 'Can you not see that I am not an ordinary creature? I am a god. One day, at a banquet in Heaven, I accidentally broke the Jade Emperor's bowl. He was very angry and I was sent down here to the River of Sands. When I am hungry, as I am now, I eat people. You would taste very good if I cut you up and put some sugar and salt on you.'

'You will not eat me! You can eat my fork!'

So again they started fighting, and they fought for two hours. After that, Pigsy pretended to be tired and ready to stop. When he left the water and climbed on to the land, the creature followed.

'Come on,' cried Pigsy. 'With the hard earth under our feet, we will have a better fight than we did before.'

'I know what you are trying to do,' said the creature. 'You are trying to get me out of the river so your friend can help you. We will go back in the water and finish the fight there.'

The creature refused to move, so they fought on the water's edge. Monkey was watching from a distance.

'Wait here,' he said to Tripitaka, 'while I try one of my tricks.'

Monkey leapt into the air and jumped straight down at the creature. But the creature saw him coming and ran back into the water.

'He is probably not going to come out again,' Monkey said.

'This is difficult,' said Pigsy. 'What are we going to do?'

'Let's go and see the Master,' said Monkey.

They told Tripitaka, who started crying loudly. 'We will never get across,' he said sadly.

'Don't worry,' Monkey said. 'It is true that we cannot get across yet. That creature is a terrible problem, but he is not going to stop us.'

'What are we going to do?' asked Pigsy.

'Pigsy,' said Monkey, 'stay here with the Master while I go to the Southern Ocean to find the Goddess Kuan-yin. This search for the Scriptures was her idea and she must help us now.'

'You had better go now,' said Tripitaka, 'and get back here quickly.'

Leaping through the clouds, Monkey reached the Southern Ocean in no time at all. He found the Goddess with the Dragon King's daughter.

'Why are you not looking after your Master?' she asked at once.

'When we came to the River of Sands,' said Monkey, 'we found a creature that we cannot destroy. He is a very good fighter. My friend Pigsy tried hard to beat him, but he was not successful. This is why I have come to you.'

'Monkey, do you ever listen? It is the same story again and again. Why did you not say that you are with the Priest of T'ang?'

'I suppose we were too busy trying to catch him,' said Monkey.

'I put him there. I intended him to help the Master and his pilgrims,' said Kuan-yin. 'You did not tell him that you were from China and looking for the Scriptures, did you? That was your mistake. He is there to help you, you fool!'

'He is sitting at the bottom of the river and he is not happy,' said Monkey. 'How can I make him come out and help us? And how is Tripitaka going to get across the river?'

Kuan-yin gave a red water-bottle to her follower Hui-yen. She told him, 'Go with Monkey to the river and shout "Sandy!" The creature will come out at once. Take him to the Master. Then put this red water-bottle in the middle of the nine heads that he wears around his neck. A ship will be sent from the Gods. It will carry Tripitaka across the River of Sands.'

Hui-yen went to the river and called, 'Sandy, Sandy! Come out and meet the Master and his pilgrims. They are looking for the Scriptures and they have been here for a long time.'

The creature came up at once. He bowed politely and asked, 'Where are the pilgrims?'

'They are sitting over there, on the eastern side,' replied Hui-yen.

'Well,' said Sandy, looking at Pigsy, 'that dirty creature never said a word about Scriptures and I fought with him for two whole days.' Then, seeing Monkey, he cried, 'Him too? I am not going near them.'

'The first is Pigsy,' said Hui-yen, 'and the second is Monkey. They are both Tripitaka's followers and both were made priests by Kuan-yin. You have nothing to fear. I myself will introduce you to the Master.'

Sandy came out of the river, tidied himself and went down on his knees in front of Tripitaka. He said, 'I did not recognise you, Master, so forgive me for being so impolite.'

'You rude creature,' said Pigsy, 'why did you want to fight with us, instead of joining us from the beginning?'

'Brother,' laughed Monkey, 'don't be angry with him, because it is all our fault. We never told him that we are going to get the Scriptures.'

'Do you really want to be a priest in our religion?' asked Tripitaka.

Sandy said that he did, so Monkey was asked to shave Sandy's head.

Monkey took a knife and soon Sandy had no hair left on his head.

Sandy bowed many times in front of Tripitaka, but only once in front of Monkey and Pigsy. Tripitaka liked Sandy's new appearance and he was very pleased with his new follower.

'You had better be quick and start your boat-building,' said Hui-yen.

Taking the heads from his neck, Sandy laid them at the edge of the water in the shape of a magic square. He put Kuan-yin's water-bottle in the middle. At once, the heads and the bottle became a ship, sent by the Gods.

Tripitaka came down to the water and walked on to the holy ship. Pigsy supported him on the left, Sandy on the right. Monkey, behind him, held on to the white horse, which followed as well as it could. They soon arrived perfectly safely at the other side.

4.1 Were you right?

Are these sentences about Tripitaka's followers right (✓) or wrong (✗)?

1 ☐ Tripitaka's horse is eaten by a dragon.

2 ☐ Goddess Kuan-yin changes the Dragon into a horse for Tripitaka.

3 ☐ She gives Monkey some magic leaves to help him.

4 ☐ She has put Pigsy on Kao's farm to prepare him to help Tripitaka.

5 ☐ Sandy's nine heads change into a red water-bottle.

4.2 What more did you learn?

Who is talking? Who to? Who or what are they talking about?

1 'Because you are so full of tricks, there is no other way to control you.'

..../...................................... ....

2 'His nose became longer, his ears became bigger, he ate more and more.'

..../...................................... ....

3 'I have been waiting for this pilgrim for years.'

..../...................................... ....

4 'For me, it will not be difficult because I can jump across in one leap.'

..../...................................... ....

5 'Then put this red water-bottle in the middle of the nine heads that he wears around his neck.'

..../...................................... ....

6 'That dirty creature never said a word about Scriptures and I fought with him for two whole days.'

..../...................................... ....

4.3 ## Language in use

Read the sentences in the box. Then write sentences with *had better*, giving advice to the pilgrims and the Goddess about the long journey.

> You **had better** stay here and look after the Master.
>
> You **had better** be quick and start your boat-building.

1 (to Tripitaka) ....

....

2 (to Monkey) ....

....

3 (to Pigsy) ....

....

4 (to Sandy) ....

....

5 (to Kuan-yin) ....

....

4.4 ## What happens next?

Read the first seven lines of Chapter 4. These pictures show the story from Tripitaka's dream. Which order do you think they come in? Number them 1–6.

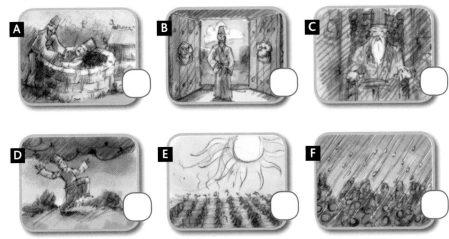

A Dead King and a Competition

Then Manjusri said a spell, the magician returned to his tiger shape,
and the God rode him away over the clouds.

Tripitaka sat in the Great Hall of the Wood Temple reciting the True Scriptures. It was midnight and he was tired. Soon he lay across his reading desk and slept. Although his eyes were closed, he seemed to know what was happening. He heard a voice outside the Hall whispering 'Master.'

Tripitaka lifted his head. In his dream he saw a man who was wet from head to foot. When he looked more closely, he saw that the man was a king. The King told Tripitaka his story:

'Five years ago, the rain stopped falling, the grass stopped growing and all my people were dying of hunger. I prayed to the Gods, but still the rivers were empty. But then a magician came who could call the wind and the rain. I asked him to pray for rain and he did. The rain came pouring down. For the next two years I was very kind to this magician. Then, in spring, when the two of us were walking by the great water hole in my palace, I suddenly saw a white light and he pushed me into the hole. He covered the top of it and then made a tree grow over it. Pity me! I have been dead for three years and nobody knows.'

Tripitaka was white with fear, but at last he said, 'Why did nobody look for you?'

'Ah, with his great power the magician transformed himself into a man who looked like me. Now he is the king of my people. But the Night Spirit blew me to you and gave me hope with talk of a great Monkey King who can kill demons with his cudgel.'

'But everybody in your country thinks that the magician is you. My follower would be attacked if he tried to help,' said Tripitaka.

'I have a son, the Prince, who spends most of his time in the Palace of Golden Bells. He is not allowed to see his mother, the Queen, because she might say something. He knows nothing about his true father except that I had this piece of white jade.'

'But how can a poor priest like me get to the Palace of Golden Bells?'

'Tomorrow my son will hunt with three thousand followers, and when you give him the jade he will know what to do. But now I must tell my Queen everything in a dream.'

As he turned to go, the dead king hit his head on the floor and Tripitaka woke up. 'Followers!' he called. 'Where are my followers?'

'Now what?' said Pigsy. 'I was happier with my old life, although the food was bad. Now I am woken up in the middle of the night to look after a priest.'

'I had a strange dream,' said Tripitaka, uncertainly.

Monkey then came in and said, 'Master, your dreams come from your waking thoughts because you worry all the time. I think only of seeing Buddha in the West, and no dream comes near me.'

But Tripitaka made Monkey listen to the dead king's story.

'Say no more,' said Monkey. 'This is work for me!'

'The King left this,' said Tripitaka, remembering, and he gave Monkey the piece of jade.

Dear Monkey! He pulled a hair from his tail, blew on it, and said a magic spell. When a beautiful small box appeared, he put the piece of jade in it.

'In the early morning,' he told Tripitaka, 'read the Scriptures in the Great Hall. I shall transform myself into a little priest, five centimetres high, and I shall jump into the box with the jade. When the Prince opens the box, I shall jump out, show him the jade and tell him the dream.'

Both the follower and his teacher were too excited to sleep that night. At last, the first light of morning came in the East. After giving whispered orders to Pigsy and Sandy to wait quietly for him, Monkey leapt into the air and flew.

At once, his red eyes found a walled city to the West. The sadness of its people hung in clouds over the city. But as Monkey was watching this sad sight, the gates opened and the huntsmen came out. It was clear from his fine clothes which huntsman was the Prince.

'Let me play a trick on him,' said Monkey to himself.

Dear Monkey! Coming down from his cloud, he transformed himself into a small woodland animal and ran in front of the Prince's horse. The Prince chased it and the huntsmen followed the Prince. Soon, Monkey had led all of them to the Wood Temple.

'Of course, I have known of this place,' said the Prince, 'although I have never visited it. I will go in.'

As the Prince and his followers went into the Great Hall, everybody welcomed him and bowed, except Tripitaka. The angry Prince told his followers to take the priest and tie him up. But Monkey, now five centimetres high and in the box, told the Gods to protect Tripitaka, so the huntsmen could not touch him.

'What magic are you using,' asked the Prince, 'to protect yourself?'

'I have no magic,' replied Tripitaka. 'I am only a priest from China, on the way to India to fetch the Scriptures. But in this box there is someone who knows something very important.'

As he spoke, Tripitaka opened the box and out leapt a very small Monkey.

The Prince laughed and said, 'What can that little creature know!'

But Monkey, to the great surprise of everybody, used his magic to return to his full size. 'Prince,' he said, 'please listen to me. Five years ago your country had no food because no rain fell, but then a magician came and he brought rain. Is this true?'

'Yes, yes, yes. Go on!'

'And what happened to the magician?'

'Three years ago, when he and my father were walking in the garden, a magic wind blew a piece of jade out of the King's hand and the magician went back to his mountains with it. But the King, my father, still misses the magician and he has locked the garden.'

Monkey laughed, but he asked the huntsmen to move away so he could speak privately to the Prince. 'Sir, it was your father who disappeared. The man in the palace is the magician who brought rain.'

'That is not true!' said the Prince.

'Here is the piece of jade,' said Monkey.

'*You* stole the jade!' shouted the Prince to the priest. 'Take him away!'

Tripitaka shouted fearfully to Monkey, 'Oh Monkey, you fool. What have you done?'

'Wait!' cried Monkey. 'I am the Monkey King and a follower of Tripitaka. Last night in this temple your father came to my Master in a dream. He told him that the magician had pushed him into a great water hole in the palace and changed into a man who looked like him. He could then pretend to be the king. I changed into a hunted animal to lead you here because I wanted to tell you this. Will you believe my story or not?' The young Prince did not know what to believe. 'Ride home,' suggested Monkey. 'Take this piece of jade with you and ask your mother, the Queen, if the present king is her husband.'

The young Prince agreed and went back to the palace. He found his mother, the Queen, still worried about a dream she had had the night before.

'Mother,' said the Prince, 'forgive my words before I speak them. Compare your life with my father in the last three years with the years before that, and tell me if his love is as warm today.'

In answer the Queen recited:

'Three years ago something warm and kind
These last three years has been as cold as ice.'

The Prince told his mother everything that he had heard that day. Then he showed her the piece of jade.

'Oh, my son,' said the Queen, 'when you came I was crying because of a dream I had last night. I dreamt I saw your father. His head was under water and he was dead. But his soul had visited a priest of T'ang and asked him to destroy the magician. He also asked him to save his own body from where it had been thrown. Go quickly and ask that priest to help us.'

The young prince ran out, jumped on his horse, rode back to the Wood Temple and asked the pilgrims to find his father. So the next night Monkey and Pigsy were at the gates of the locked Flower Garden. But Monkey had told Pigsy that there was gold at the bottom of the water hole. He had said nothing about the dead king.

Pigsy brought his fork down on the lock of the gates and broke it. Inside the garden, Monkey could not stop himself jumping and shouting happily.

'Brother,' said Pigsy, 'you will ruin us, making all that noise!'

'Why are you trying to make me nervous?' said Monkey.

They found the tree that the magician had planted on top of the hole. 'Now, Pigsy, the gold is hidden under this tree,' said Monkey.

At once, the fool Pigsy hit the tree with his fork until it fell down. Then he used his nose to dig under it until, about a metre down, he found a big stone. 'Brother!' he cried. 'This is luck. The gold will be under this.'

Pigsy used his nose again and lifted the big stone. Below it something was shining. 'That is the gold!' cried Pigsy. But looking closer, they saw it was the light of the stars and the moon in the water.

Monkey made his cudgel grow until it was ten metres long, and Pigsy climbed down it. When he was in the water, he began to swim. Monkey called down to him, 'The gold is at the bottom.'

So Pigsy dived down and, opening his eyes again, saw a door with a sign on it that said *The Palace at the Bottom of the Water Hole*. Pigsy went in and a servant called out, 'Great King, something awful has happened – a priest with a long nose has come in.'

The Dragon King of the Water Hole was not surprised. 'That must be Pigsy,' he explained. 'He has come with the Monkey King to find the dishonest magician. Please come in and sit down,' he called to Pigsy.

Pigsy, happy and wet, sat in the best seat and asked, 'Where is the gold?'

'I am sorry,' said the Dragon King, 'but I live down here in this hole and never see the sky above. Where would I get gold from?'

'Oh, please!' said Pigsy. 'I know it is here somewhere, so you had better bring it out.'

'I have one thing that is of value. You can look,' said the Dragon King. He led Pigsy to the body of the dead king. Pigsy went back up to Monkey. Monkey told him that the body was better than gold. So Pigsy dived back down again and brought the body up.

Monkey looked closely at the body, which had been dead for three years. He asked Pigsy, 'After three years, how can it still look so fresh?'

'The Dragon King used a magic stone to keep it like that,' Pigsy answered.

'That was a bit of luck,' said Monkey. 'But we must still get his enemy and make him pay for this terrible murder. And we will be thanked for our good work. Quickly, Pigsy, carry the King away.'

'Where to?' asked Pigsy.

'To the temple,' said Monkey, 'to show him to Tripitaka.'

'What an idea!' Pigsy complained to himself. 'I was tricked into doing this job. I do not want to carry this dead body.'

'Hurry, Pigsy,' said Monkey impatiently.

'I am not going to carry it,' said Pigsy.

'If you do not want to be beaten, you will carry it away now,' said Monkey.

Pigsy feared the cudgel, so he lifted up the dead body and put it on his back.

'This Monkey,' he said to himself, 'has played a dirty trick on me, but he will be sorry. When we get back to the temple, I will tell Tripitaka that Monkey can bring the dead to life. Monkey will say that he cannot. And I will tell Tripitaka to recite the spell. Monkey's head will hurt, but I will not be happy until his brains shoot out of his head.'

They took the body back to the temple and showed it to Tripitaka. He told Monkey to bring it back to life.

'Only Yama, King of Death, can do that,' said Monkey.

'Don't believe him!' cried Pigsy. 'Just tighten that cap on his head.'

Poor Monkey! He was soon holding his head in great pain as Tripitaka recited the spell. The cap became tighter and tighter.

'But Master,' said Monkey, 'what will happen if I fail?'

'If someone puts a good breath into him, he will be himself again, even after three years under water,' said Tripitaka.

Pigsy at once offered his breath, but Tripitaka knew that it was not pure. Pigsy had eaten the bodies of humans. So he asked for Monkey, whose food had been only apples and food from the forest. Monkey blew hard into the King's mouth and his soul returned.

Then they all went back to the city to find the magician who had taken the appearance of the King. When they were led to him, they refused to bow.

'And who are you?' asked the false king, surprised.

'My Master,' said Monkey, 'is called Tripitaka and he is like a younger brother to the Emperor of China. I am his main follower.' Then he told the false king about Pigsy and Sandy, but he introduced the true king as a temple servant.

The false king wanted to know more about this 'temple servant'. He looked at the true king, who was afraid of him, but Monkey whispered, 'It is all right! I will speak for you.'

Dear Monkey! He stepped forwards and cried to the magician in a loud, clear voice. 'Oh, King, this old man has had some hard times in his life. Five years ago, disaster came to his family when Heaven sent no rain and people died because there was no water. Then from the mountains came a magician who helped the people. But he then destroyed this man's life. He pushed him into a great water hole in the palace and became a false king of the people. But I have returned life to the dead man and he should be king again – not this magician.'

The magician felt fear deep in his heart. Taking a sword from a soldier, he jumped on a cloud and disappeared.

Both Sandy and Pigsy were very angry. 'Now we will never be able to find him,' they shouted.

Dear Monkey! Telling Pigsy and Sandy to take good care of the Prince, the King, his ministers, the Queen and Tripitaka, he suddenly leapt into the clouds. Looking down, he saw the magician running to the North-east. He shouted, 'Where do you think you are going? Monkey has come!'

'Keep out of my way,' shouted the magician.

Monkey fought a terrible fight with his cudgel against the magician and his sword, but suddenly the magician escaped back to the city. He transformed himself into someone who looked like Tripitaka. Monkey followed him but did not dare use his cudgel.

'Which is the real Tripitaka?' he shouted to Pigsy and Sandy.

'We do not know,' they answered. 'We have no idea.'

'Master, recite your spell,' called Monkey.

The real Tripitaka at once recited. Pigsy lifted up his fork as the magician flew up into the air. Dear Pigsy! He chased the magician, with Sandy and Monkey close behind him.

What a fight there was then, with three wild priests hitting and kicking at one terrible ugly creature again and again. In the end, Monkey leapt above the creature, and he was going to cut him in half with his cudgel when a voice said, 'Monkey, stop the fight.'

It was the God Manjusri. He had come down from Heaven with a magic mirror which showed demons in their true form.

'But I do not understand,' said Monkey. 'In this mirror, the magician is a tiger.'

'Yes,' said Manjusri. 'As a magician, he was acting under Buddha's orders.'

'What!' cried Monkey. 'The magician is protected by Buddha! How can that be?'

'Let me explain,' said Manjusri. 'In the beginning, the true king pleased Buddha so much that he sent me to fetch him to the Western Heaven. But I said something to the King that offended him. He told his soldiers to throw me into the river. Then Buddha sent this magician to throw the King into the water hole for three years. But now, with your help, he has been forgiven.'

'Yes, but the people of the city?' asked Monkey.

'Nothing has happened to them. During these three years, rain has fallen and there has been peace.'

'And the Queen, who has slept with him as his wife?'

'He has not been a husband to her,' was the answer. 'He is not a whole man.'

'Then take him away,' said Monkey. 'He can thank you for saving him.'

Manjusri said a spell, the magician returned to his tiger shape, and the God rode him away over the clouds.

As the pilgrims travelled further on their journey to the West, they heard a noise that sounded like a thousand voices.

Dear Monkey! He leapt high into the clouds, looked down, and at a little distance he saw a hill outside a city. There, a great crowd of Buddhist priests were carrying bricks and wood for building. They were hot and tired and crying out to the God of Power to give them strength.

'They are going to build a temple,' thought Monkey. But suddenly the gates of the city opened and two Taoist* priests came out. Monkey saw at once that the Buddhists were afraid of them. He thought, 'This must be the city I have heard about. The religion of Buddha has been destroyed here.'

Monkey transformed himself into a Taoist magician, walked towards the two young Taoist priests and bowed low.

'Can a poor Taoist find food in this city?'

'Oh, yes,' said the priests. 'Even the King is pleased to give food to Taoists. Twenty years ago there was not enough food in this place and it was saved by three Taoist Immortals who came out of the sky. They can bring wind or rain or turn stones into gold.'

* Taoist: of an Eastern religion and way of life that, like Buddhism, was important in China and still is in a number of Asian countries

'Your king is lucky to have these Immortals here. I would like to meet him.'

'That is no problem,' said the priests. 'But first we must count those Buddhists and check that they are working well.'

'But they are priests, like us! We should not make them work.'

'Well, when we had no food, the Buddhists prayed to Buddha with no success at all. We Taoists prayed to our gods and we were successful. So they are not really priests and we should really destroy their temples. But now they work for us as builders and cleaners.'

'Then I cannot meet your masters,' Monkey said, 'because I am looking for an uncle who became a Buddhist priest.'

'That is no problem,' they replied. 'Take our list and check while we wait here. See if your uncle is among our priests.'

As Monkey walked towards the priests with the list, they all went down on their knees in front of him.

'Please don't harm us, Father!' they said. 'We have all worked hard and we have never been ill or missed work.'

Monkey told them to get up. He said that they did not need to fear him – he was only looking for his uncle.

Hearing this, they all crowded near him. 'Which of us do you want?' they asked.

Monkey laughed. 'You are priests!' he said. 'Why do you work as servants instead of reading the Scriptures?'

'Ah, don't laugh at us,' cried the priests. 'Our King has chosen other masters and we do what they tell us. The three Immortals are very powerful and can perform a lot of magic. Now they are using magic to keep the King young. That is why he obeys them.'

'Why do you not run away?' asked Monkey.

'There are pictures of us in every part of the country and there are police everywhere. Many of us have taken our own lives. But the spirits tell us that one day a pilgrim will come and with him is a follower called the Monkey King. He will use his great powers to right wrongs, and he will free us.'

Monkey went back to the two Taoist priests. They asked him if he had found his relative.

'They are all relatives of mine,' replied Monkey. 'Two hundred on my father's side and three hundred on my mother's. I would like you to free them.'

'We cannot do that!' said the priests. 'One or two of them can stop work if they are ill, but all of them? Impossible! You must be mad!'

'Really?' said Monkey and, taking his cudgel, he killed them where they stood.

The Buddhists came running. 'Oh, what have you done!' they said. 'The people will say that we killed the priests! You must come to the King at once and explain that you are responsible.'

'I am not what you think I am,' said Monkey. 'I am the one who has come to free you.'

'But you are a murderer!' said the Buddhist priests. 'The spirits described the one who will free us. He has a flat head, bright red eyes, a hairy face and no chin.'

Monkey transformed himself back from a Taoist priest into himself, and the Buddhists bowed in front of him.

'Now go away from here!' cried Monkey. 'But first I shall give you some protecting magic.'

Dear Monkey! He pulled out a handful of his hairs, bit them into pieces and gave a small piece to each of the Buddhists.

'Put this behind your ear. If you are in any danger, press your ear and call out "Monkey King!" I will come at once to help you, even if I am thousands of kilometres away.'

Some of the braver priests tested the hairs and called out 'Monkey King!' At once a thunder god with a great cudgel appeared. 'If you say "Quiet", he will disappear,' Monkey told them. And at the word 'Quiet', he disappeared.

'Don't go far from this place and there will be news for you soon,' Monkey called as the priests departed. He left to tell Tripitaka what had happened.

As the pilgrims entered the city, some people were afraid of them. But an old Buddhist priest recognised Monkey and shouted, 'I have dreamt of you, Monkey King. Thanks to you, we are not ghosts – we are living men.'

That night, Monkey's head was so full of plans for the next day that he could not sleep. He got up, looked down into the street and saw that the Taoists were all celebrating in the temple. They were led by the three Immortals.

At once, Monkey went to find Pigsy and Sandy. 'Come and have some fun,' he whispered in Sandy's ear.

'Who wants fun in the middle of the night?' said Sandy, sleepily.

'The Taoist Temple has plenty of food in it,' said Monkey. 'Bread, cake, fruit, sweets ...'

Pigsy woke up at the sound of a list of food. 'Brother, I am coming too,' he cried.

When they arrived at the temple, Pigsy could not wait. 'They are all still praying!' he complained.

'I will soon stop that,' said Monkey, and he blew hard. A great wind passed through the temple, blowing everything on to the ground and putting all the lights out. Frightened in the dark, all the Taoists ran away.

The three pilgrims went inside and the three of them finished all the food.

But a little Taoist remembered that he had left his hand-bell in the temple and went back for it. He opened the door and saw that all the food was gone. He ran away to fetch the three Immortals.

When they came, one of them thought that their gods had eaten the food.

'Let's pray to them,' the Immortal said, 'for long life for the King.'

Then Monkey jumped out and called to them. 'How could you be such fools?' he said. 'We are not gods, we are priests from China. We have eaten all your food and your king will have to go somewhere else for a long life.'

The Taoist Immortals attacked the pilgrims, but Monkey took Sandy in one hand and Pigsy in the other and leapt on to a cloud with them. In no time, they were back in their beds, in the hotel where they were staying with Tripitaka.

Next day, the King was very angry when he heard that three Buddhist pilgrims wanted to see him. But one of his ministers stepped forward.

'The country of T'ang is fifty thousand kilometres away,' he said. 'If they really come from there, they must have magic powers. Let's hear them.'

So the King allowed the pilgrims to come in, but before they could speak, three important Taoists came in and made a report to the King.

'Yesterday,' they said, 'these three killed two of our followers and helped five hundred Buddhist priests to escape. That night, they went into our temple and ate all the food.'

The angry King ordered the immediate death of the three pilgrims. But before anyone could do anything about the order, some men arrived asking urgently for rain. The King thought about the pilgrims' magic powers.

'There will be a rain-making competition between you and the Immortals,' he said to the pilgrims. 'If you win, you will go free. If you lose, you will die!'

A tower was quickly built and the King, the pilgrims and the Immortals went outside.

'You must say what you are going to pray for,' said Monkey to an Immortal. 'How else will we know if you are successful?'

When the King heard Monkey's words, he said, 'This little priest is a sensible Monkey.'

'There is no need to tell you,' said the Immortal. 'The King knows what I am going to do.'

'That is not what I mean. We must each have our programme. If we do not, we will get confused.'

'Yes, fine. I shall cry out four times,' said the Immortal. 'At the first cry, wind will come; at the second, clouds will appear in the sky; at the third, you will hear thunder; at the fourth, rain will fall. But I shall cry out once more and the rain will stop.'

'Please begin,' said Monkey. 'This will be very entertaining for us.'

The tower was ten metres high. On each side there were the twenty-eight flags of the Great House of the Moon. There was a long table with burners on it, which gave a sweet-smelling smoke. There was a metal plate with the name of the thunder-spirit written on it next to each burner. At the foot of the table there were five great bowls of clear water with flowers in them. Behind the tower were some Taoists writing down religious teachings.

The Immortal went to the tower and climbed to the top. With his sword in his hand, he recited spells, and a strong wind was heard and felt in the air above.

'That is bad,' whispered Pigsy. 'He is winning.'

'Quiet, Brother,' whispered Monkey, 'and leave it to me.'

Dear Monkey! He leapt into the air and cried, 'Who is in charge of the wind?'

At once, the Old Woman of the Wind appeared.

'I am protecting Tripitaka on his way to India,' said Monkey. 'We are having a rain-making competition with the Immortals here. Why are you helping them instead of us? Stop that wind!' cried Monkey, and immediately the wind stopped.

The Immortal now hit the tower hard and the sky filled with clouds.

'Who is in charge of the clouds?' cried Monkey, and the Cloud Boy appeared in front of him. 'Stop the clouds!' he commanded, and again the sky became clear.

The Immortal loosened his hair and then knocked again on the tower. The Thunder God and the Mother of Lightning appeared in the sky, but they bowed towards Monkey.

'The Jade Emperor in Heaven,' they said, 'ordered us to make a storm.'

'You are allowed to do that,' said Monkey, 'but not yet.'

As there was no thunder and no lightning, the Immortal was confused as well as angry.

'Listen well,' said Monkey, up in the sky. 'Here are my orders. When I point my cudgel upwards once, you will give me wind. Twice, and you will give me clouds. Three times, thunder and lightning. And four times, rain. 'And when I point it a fifth time, you will stop the storm.'

The Immortal sadly left the tower and went to speak to the King.

'I have been watching,' said the King. 'You have not produced either wind or rain. What is wrong?'

'The rain-dragons are not at home today,' said the Immortal.

'Don't believe him!' cried Monkey. 'They are all at home. That Immortal has no real power over them. We, the followers of Buddha, will soon put them to work. You will see!'

'Go to the tower,' said the King to Monkey. 'I will wait here and see if there is any rain.'

'I need your help too,' said Monkey to Tripitaka. 'Go quietly to the tower and start reciting your Scriptures.'

'My dear friend,' said Tripitaka, 'I do not know anything about making rain!'

'Don't let him pull you into this,' whispered Pigsy to Tripitaka. 'He will blame you if no rain comes.'

'It is true that you do not know how to make rain,' said Monkey to Tripitaka. 'But you know how to recite the Scriptures. If you do that, I will do the rest.'

Tripitaka went up the tower, sat down and began silently reciting. Then Monkey took his cudgel from behind his ear, and made it bigger until it was nearly a metre long. He pointed it towards the sky.

The Old Woman of the Wind brought out her bag and when she opened it, a great wind rushed out of it. It blew through the city, lifting stones and rocks high into the air. Monkey pointed again and a black cloud covered the sky, so the people of the city could not even see their palace. He pointed again and loud thunder shook the Earth. When he pointed a fourth time, rain fell down until it seemed that the Yellow River had fallen out of the sky. In seconds, the whole city was under water.

The people of the city were filled with terror and they all began saying their prayers. The rain fell from early morning until midday.

'Enough!' cried the King. 'Stop the rain or nothing will grow this year!'

Monkey at once pointed a fifth time with his cudgel and the storm stopped. There was not even a cloud in the sky.

'Wonderful priests!' cried the happy King. 'So it is true! There is always a stronger magic than the strongest! In the past we have seen our Immortals bring rain successfully. But even they could not stop it suddenly. Light rain always continued for the rest of the day. But these priests stopped the rain completely!'

The Immortal began making excuses.

'You said that the rain-dragons were not at home,' the King said, 'and that made it impossible to get rain. But look! The Buddhists, in their quiet way, made the rain fall. *They* were successful, not you.'

Again, the Immortal tried to change the King's mind, but Monkey jumped in front of him and spoke to the King.

'Sir, the Dragon Kings made the wind, the clouds and the rain. They are still in the sky, so would you like to see them?'

'Of course!' cried the King. 'I have been king for a long time, but I have never seen a dragon. I will reward anyone who can show me one. But if you do not produce a dragon, you will be punished.'

The Taoists knew quite well that this was beyond their powers. They tried, but no dragon answered their call. Then it was Monkey's turn.

'Are you there?' Monkey called up into the sky. 'Let's have a look at you and your brothers.'

When the four Dragon Kings immediately appeared through the clouds, the King began to burn sweet-smelling sticks. His ministers went down on their knees in front of them.

'I feel ashamed,' said the King. 'I have troubled them for no reason. Tell them that I do not want to trouble them any more. I will find an opportunity to repay them soon with offerings.'

'Spirits, you can leave us now,' said Monkey. 'The King will repay you with offerings at the earliest opportunity.'

The Dragons flew off, each to his own ocean, and again the sky was clear.

The King gave orders for a banquet the next day, to thank the pilgrims. All the Buddhists were invited to return to the city, and they were welcomed to the banquet by the King himself.

After the banquet, the Buddhist priests took the pilgrims to the gates of the city, and they gave Monkey back the hairs he had given them. Then Monkey said, 'Now you can see that Buddhism is the True Way, but you must obey all priests – Taoist priests too – and become better men. Then these hills and streams will be safe for ever.'

The King himself rode out with the pilgrims far beyond the city's walls, where they said goodbye.

5.1 Were you right?

Look at your answers to Activity 4.4. Then put these events from the story in the correct order. Write 1–7.

a ☐ The King gives Tripitaka a piece of white jade to show to the Prince.

b ☐ When the Queen sees the jade, she describes her dream to her son.

c ☐ Manjusri explains that the false king killed the true King under Buddha's orders.

d 1 The dead King appears in Tripitaka's dream, telling him about his death at the hands of the magician.

e ☐ Monkey and Pigsy fight with the false king until they are stopped by the god Manjusri.

f ☐ Manjusri's spell returns the magician to his true form, a tiger.

g ☐ Monkey changes himself into a hunted animal so the Prince will chase him and they can talk about the King.

5.2 What more did you learn?

Write *Buddhist* or *Taoist* in the sentences below.

1 Monkey looks down from a cloud and sees a great crowd of .... priests carrying bricks and wood for a temple.

2 The religion of Buddha has been destroyed in this city by .... priests.

3 Monkey transforms himself into a .... magician and asks for food.

4 The .... priests are waiting for the Monkey King to free them.

5 After the pilgrims eat all the food in the .... Temple, the .... Immortals attack them.

6 Monkey and his friends help five hundred .... priests to escape.

5.3 Language in use

Read the sentences in the box. Then complete the sentences below with past perfect verb forms.

> The magician **had pushed** him into a great water hole in the palace.
>
> The Prince told his mother everything that he **had heard** that day.

1 The Queen was still worried about a dream that she .... (have) the night before.

2 In the Queen's dream, the King's soul .... (visit) a priest of T'ang and asked him to destroy the magician.

3 Pigsy was happy to go down the water-hole because Monkey .... (tell) him that there was gold at the bottom.

4 When the three Immortals arrived at their temple, one of them thought that their gods .... (eat) the food.

5 Rain fell until it seemed that the Yellow River .... (fall) out of the sky.

6 After the banquet, the Buddhist priests gave Monkey back the hairs that he .... (give) them.

5.4 What happens next?

Look at the first four pictures in Chapter 5. Write a sentence about each picture and give a possible explanation for what is happening.

1 ....

....

2 ....

....

3 ....

....

4 ....

....

The River to Heaven

'What has happened to Tripitaka?' shouted Monkey from the air.
'There is no Tripitaka now!' Pigsy shouted back.

They travelled without stopping for many days. Then Tripitaka stopped his horse and said to Monkey, 'Follower, when and where are we going to rest?'

'Comfort,' answered Monkey, 'is for ordinary people, so pilgrims cannot expect it. By day or by night, in wet or dry weather, if there is a road to travel, we must continue.'

Soon Sandy shouted, 'There is a great river in front of us!'

'Wait here!' cried Monkey, leaping high into the air. Soon he was back. 'I cannot see land on the other side,' he said, 'but I thought I saw a fisherman. He was standing at the water's edge. I will ask him about the river.'

But it was not a fisherman that Monkey had seen. It was a sign that said: *The River That Leads to Heaven. Few people have reached the other side.*

When Tripitaka read this, he cried quietly. 'I knew so little of the difficulties in our way, on the road to India,' he said.

'Listen,' said Pigsy. 'That music means there are priests praying somewhere near here. They will tell us how we can get across the river.'

Following the sound, they soon saw a village of several hundred houses. One of them had a flag at its gate and lights outside.

'I shall go in first,' said Tripitaka, 'because you three look a little strange and I do not want people to be frightened.'

An old man came to the door and when he saw Tripitaka he said, 'You have come a little late. The banquet is almost finished and there is not much to eat.'

'I did not come for the banquet,' answered Tripitaka. 'I have come from China and I would like a bed for the night if that is possible.'

'China is a very long way away,' said the old man, whose name was Ch'en. 'How do I know that your words are true?'

'My three followers have helped me on the journey. They have made it possible for me to travel so far.'

'Well, they had better come in with you.'

The three pilgrims came rushing in out of the dark, leading the white horse, carrying the luggage and shouting. The old man fell on the floor, crying, 'Demons! Help! Demons!'

'Not demons,' said Tripitaka, 'but my followers. I know they are ugly, but they are very good at fighting tigers, dragons and other creatures.'

A group of praying priests jumped up and ran away in fear. The pilgrims laughed so loudly at this that the priests ran even faster.

'You fools!' cried Tripitaka to his followers. 'I have tried so hard to teach you to behave correctly! Learn this: It is admirable to be good without being taught. It is normal to be good after being taught. Only a *fool* is taught and then is *still* bad. Do you not understand that I will have to take the blame for this?'

The three stood silently, so the old man believed that they really were followers of Tripitaka. He sat Tripitaka in the best place at the table, and food was brought for them all. Tripitaka began to recite the Scripture Before Eating, but Pigsy poured all the food into his mouth from the bowl before Tripitaka had finished.

As Pigsy was calling 'More food, more food' to the servants, the old man spoke to Tripitaka. 'Did you read the sign by the river? You were quite near the Temple of the Great King of Magic,' he said. 'He is the god who sends us rain. He makes things grow.' But as he spoke, he began to cry loudly.

'Why are you crying when you speak of the God?' asked Monkey.

'That god is an angry god and every year he takes the life of a boy and a girl, so we have few children here. I have one child, a son called War Boy, and my brother has one girl, called Much Gold. This year our family must give the children to the God and both of them must die.'

'Let me see the boy,' said Monkey.

The boy was brought down from his bed and ran around eating fruit. Without a word, Monkey transformed himself into a boy who looked exactly the same.

'That is unbelievable,' cried the father. 'Look! When I call, *both* come running to me.'

Monkey then changed back to his own form. 'I am going to save this child's life,' he said to the father. 'I will let the Great King of Magic kill me for the gods.'

The old man's brother was standing in the doorway, watching and crying.

'I think you are worried about your daughter,' said Monkey.

'Father,' said the old man, 'I cannot lose her. She is my only child. Who will cry for me when I die?'

Monkey pointed at Pigsy. 'If you feed that long-nosed brother of mine enough,' he said, 'he will transform himself into your girl and do anything else you ask. The Great King of Magic can kill us both together.'

Pigsy was shocked. 'Leave me out of this!' he said.

'You know what they say,' said Monkey. '"Even a chicken must work for its food."'

'I am no good at transformations,' complained Pigsy. 'I can change into a mountain or a tree, but it is much more difficult to change into a small girl.'

'Don't believe him,' said Monkey to the girl's father. 'Bring your child.'

Soon the man returned with his child, and all the priests and servants asked Pigsy to save her.

'Here she is,' said Monkey. 'Have a look and be quick.'

The fool Pigsy shook his head, said a spell and cried 'Change!' His head was now the same as the child's but his big stomach had not changed.

'You can hit me if you like,' complained Pigsy, 'but I cannot do any better than that.'

'I can see that I will have to help,' said Monkey. And he blew on Pigsy, who was soon like the child from head to foot.

'What happens now?' asked Monkey. 'How are we brought to the God?'

The girl's father came forward. 'It is quite simple,' he said. 'You sit in two dishes, two men carry you to the temple, and then the Great King of Magic eats you.'

'Watch me,' Monkey said to Pigsy. 'While he is cutting me into pieces, you can run away.'

'But he might begin with the girl!' cried Pigsy.

'No,' said War Boy's father quietly. 'The meal always begins with the boy.'

'Well, that is lucky,' said Pigsy.

Suddenly, they all saw lights outside and heard the sound of voices as the gate opened. A loud voice cried, 'Bring out the boy and the girl!'

The two fathers cried while the Great King's servants carried the boy and the girl away.

'Great King,' said the villagers, when everything was ready, 'we now offer you a boy child, War Boy, and a girl child, Much Gold, with a pig, a sheep and some wine.' They then went back to their homes.

'I think I will go home too,' said Pigsy.

'You *have* no home,' said Monkey. 'What rubbish you talk! We have started this job and now we have to finish it.'

Just then, a strong wind blew through the door, and as it opened the Great King appeared. He was a horrible creature, with eyes like fire and teeth like a pig.

'Which family do you come from?' asked the Great King.

'The family of Ch'en,' answered Monkey.

The King did not understand why the boy was so brave. Usually the children were too frightened to talk before they were killed.

'You understand that I am now going to eat you?'

'Do it!' said Monkey.

'You are too brave,' said the Great King. 'This time I shall begin with the girl.'

'No, no!' said Pigsy. 'It is never a good idea to change an old custom. Do what you usually do – that is always best.'

The fool leapt off his dish, changed back into Pigsy, took his fork and hit the Great King. Then he and Monkey leapt into the air, just as the Great King changed into a wind and disappeared into the river.

'Oh, let him go now,' said Monkey. 'We will finish him tomorrow and get our Master across the river.'

So they returned to Ch'en's farm, where they were soon asleep in the best room in the house.

But under the river, the Great King was unhappy. He told his fish-servants what had happened. He told them about Tripitaka, who was like a god. If somebody ate him, they would never die.

The Great King's fish-sister made a suggestion. 'Start a cold wind and a great fall of snow, so the river freezes. Then some of us will change into human form and walk across it, carrying luggage. Tripitaka is in such a hurry to get to India that he will walk across it too. When you hear him above you, heat the ice. The pilgrims will fall through it and you will have them all.'

Just before the sun came up, Tripitaka and his followers began to feel cold.

'Pilgrims,' said Monkey, 'should not feel either heat or cold.'

But they could not sleep, and when they looked out of the window everything was white. The snow was so lovely that they sat and watched it fall. It was like small pieces of white jade.

Soon servants brought them hot water to wash in, hot tea to drink and hot food to eat. They even brought heaters for the rooms, but when the meal was finished the pilgrims were colder than ever. By now there was nearly a metre of snow outside and, seeing this, Tripitaka began to cry.

But towards evening everyone was talking about the river. It had frozen and people were walking on the ice. The next morning the ice was even thicker and Tripitaka gave thanks to the Gods for this chance to walk across the river.

'Master,' said Sandy, 'should we not wait until the ice goes away? Then we can go across the river in Mr Ch'en's boat.'

'But if we wait until the spring,' said Tripitaka, 'we will lose half a year's travelling. I promised the Goddess Kuan-yin that the journey would take three years. Already seven have passed.'

He ordered Pigsy to put the luggage on the horse, and they left.

When they had gone fifteen or twenty kilometres across the ice, Pigsy showed Tripitaka how to carry his stick across his body.

'Ice often has holes in it,' he explained. 'If you put your foot in a hole, you will go down into the water. It will close above you and you will never get out again. Carry your stick across your body and you will feel safer.'

Monkey looked disbelieving, but they all did as Pigsy had said.

They rode all night until the sun began to come up. Then they stopped to eat some food from their luggage and then continued towards the West.

But after some time, the ice began to break and the white horse almost fell.

They continued walking, not knowing that the Great King and his fish-followers were waiting below. Suddenly, a great hole opened in the ice. Monkey at once leapt high into the air, but the white horse and all the others fell through it. The Great King took Tripitaka and carried him down to the Great Palace under the water.

'Where is my fish-sister?' said the Great King. 'Come, fetch the sharp knives. Let's eat Tripitaka and live for ever.'

'Great King,' answered the Fish-Sister. 'Let's wait for a couple of days until we can be sure that his followers cannot spoil our fun.'

The King agreed, and Tripitaka was put in a great stone box at the back of the palace.

At the same time, Pigsy and Sandy had managed to get the luggage out of the water and put it on to the horse's back. They started swimming back the way they had come.

'What has happened to Tripitaka?' shouted Monkey from the air.

'There is no Tripitaka now!' Pigsy shouted back. 'We are going back to Ch'en's farm.'

Mr Ch'en cried uncontrollably when he heard what had happened to Tripitaka.

'Don't worry,' said Monkey. 'I think the Master will live for a long time. Let's dry our clothes and then we will go back and finish that creature!'

Back at the river, Monkey asked Pigsy to carry him down while Sandy swam behind them. And at the bottom of the river they found a gate with the sign **Turtle** *House* written on it.

Monkey whispered, 'You two hide at each side of the door!' Then he changed

turtle /'tɜːtl/ (n) an animal that lives in water most of the time. It has a hard back, into which it can put its head and legs for protection.

himself into a fish and swam inside. The Great King and his fish-followers were talking about eating Tripitaka, but Monkey could not see his Master. Then he heard Tripitaka crying inside a stone box.

'Don't worry,' said Monkey, 'we will soon get you out.'

'Be quick! Oh, be quick!' cried Tripitaka from inside his box.

'I am going now,' said Monkey, 'but I shall return.' And soon he and Pigsy and Sandy were back at the riverbank.

'I am not at my best in the water, so it is not a good plan for me to go down again and fight the Great King,' said Monkey. 'I shall go to the Goddess of the Southern Ocean for help. I shall not waste a minute.'

Dear Monkey! He shot up in the air on a magic light, leapt on a cloud and found Kuan-yin. She was expecting him, but had not finished getting dressed.

'Let's leave now,' she said, when she saw Monkey. 'We will go and save Tripitaka.'

Monkey went down on his knees in front of her. 'Do you not want to finish dressing first?' he asked.

'It is too much trouble,' she answered. 'I am going like this.'

She left on her cloud, followed by Monkey.

'Well, that was quick!' said Pigsy, as they appeared. 'You did well to get a goddess to come immediately, before she had even finished combing her hair!'

The Goddess sailed low over the river like a cloud. Untying the belt from her dress, she tied a basket to it and pulled the basket through the water. She repeated the words, 'The dead go, the living stay,' seven times and pulled the basket up. There was a gold fish in it. Its tail moved and its eye stared.

'Go at once into the water and fetch your Master,' said the Goddess to Monkey.

'But what shall I do with the Great King?' asked Monkey.

'The Great King is in the basket,' said the Goddess. 'He used to live in a little pool in my garden. Every day he used to put his head out and listen to the Scriptures, until at last he held great magical powers. But one day there was a great storm and the water took him far out to sea. I thought that he might be using his magic against your Master. So without stopping to comb my hair, I made this magic basket to catch him in.'

'If you want to make humans believe in the Gods,' said Monkey, 'you will wait here. I will call the people of the village to hear this story and look at your golden face.'

So men and women, young and old, were soon hurrying to the river to go down on their knees in front of the Goddess. One of them later painted a famous painting called *Kuan-yin with the Fish Basket*.

When the Goddess had returned to the Southern Ocean, Pigsy and Sandy dived down to the Great King's palace. All the Great King's fish-followers were dead, so they soon helped Tripitaka out of the stone box and took him back to Ch'en's farm.

'We are sorry, Sirs,' said the Ch'en brothers, 'that you had so many problems.'

'Oh, that is all finished now,' said Monkey. 'The important thing is that next year, and every other year, your village will not lose its children. But we would be glad if you could give us a boat to carry us across the river.'

All the villagers started to make boats. But when the pilgrims went back to the river, they heard a voice: 'Oh, great Monkey King, you do not need to build a boat. I will take you.' And above the waters they saw the white head and the enormous body of a turtle.

'You!' cried Monkey. 'You demon! If you come near us, I will kill you with my cudgel.'

'Great Monkey King,' said the turtle, 'listen to me. I am not a follower of the Great King. His palace below the river used to be mine. Then one day that creature came swimming into the river. killed many of my family and made the others work for him. I am grateful for all that you have done – you have made us free again.'

'Promise me and promise the Gods that this is all true,' said Monkey.

The turtle opened his red mouth wide. 'I promise you and all the Gods. If I do not take Tripitaka safely across the river, my bones will turn to water.'

The turtle came out of the river, and people saw that his back was fifteen metres wide.

'Climb on the turtle's back,' called Monkey to the others. 'He has promised that we will be safe. When creatures speak human language, their words are usually true.'

The white horse was led to the middle

of the turtle's back. Tripitaka stood to the left, Sandy to the right, and Pigsy behind the horse's tail. Monkey put himself in front of the horse's head.

'Now, turtle,' he cried. 'Go gently, because if you do not, there will be a cudgel on your head!'

With this warning, the turtle moved smoothly over the water. As the pilgrims left, all the people of the village bowed and thanked Buddha.

The turtle travelled quickly, and in less than a day they had arrived at the other side.

Tripitaka said to the turtle, 'I have nothing that I can give you. But I would like to thank you for taking us across the river.'

'Master,' replied the turtle, 'there is something that you could do for me. I have been trying to become perfect for about a thousand years, and that is a long time. I can now use human speech, but I am still a turtle. Please ask the Buddha if I can become a human.'

Tripitaka gladly promised to ask Buddha the question, and the turtle swam back to his home in the river.

Again Pigsy carried the luggage, and Monkey helped Tripitaka on to the white horse. With Sandy behind them, they soon found the road to the West.

They travelled for many months. The country was very different from anything they had seen before. The flowers were like jewels, the grass looked magical and there were strange and wonderful trees.

In every village, families were entertaining priests. On every hill, Immortals were practising control over their bodies. In every wood, pilgrims were reciting and singing.

Every night, they found somewhere to stay and left again at the first light of day. They travelled on in this way for many more days until suddenly the light grew bright and they saw a wonderful castle.

'Monkey,' said Tripitaka admiringly, pointing at it, 'that's a fine place!'

'Do you remember,' said Monkey, 'how often on our journey you have bowed in front of the caves and hiding-places and palaces of false magicians? It is strange that you do not even get off your horse now – when you see the Buddha's holy castle!'

So Tripitaka, in great excitement, jumped down from his horse. When they reached the gates, a young priest came out to greet them.

He asked, 'Are you the pilgrims who have come from the East for the Scriptures?'

The boy was dressed in beautiful clothes and carried a bowl of jade dust in his hand. Monkey knew him at once, and turned to Tripitaka.

'This,' he said, 'is the Golden-Headed Immortal of the Jade Temple at the foot of the Holy Mountain.'

'Here you are at last!' said the Golden-Headed Immortal. 'It is now ten years since the Goddess Kuan-yin told me to expect your arrival. Year after year I have waited, but there has been no sign!'

'Great Immortal,' said Tripitaka, bowing low, 'I cannot thank you enough for your patience.'

Inside the temple, sweet-smelling hot water was brought to wash in, and after supper the pilgrims were shown to their beds.

Early the next day, Tripitaka put on his finest clothes and jewellery and greeted the young Immortal.

'That is better,' said the young Immortal. 'Yesterday you looked rather untidy, but today you look like a true child of Buddha! You must let me show you the way. Monkey knows it, but only by air, and you must travel on the ground.'

Taking Tripitaka by the hand, he led the pilgrims through the temple gardens to the back of the building and up a path to the hill behind.

'Do you see that mountain in front of you?' said the young Immortal, pointing up. 'That is where Buddha has his home. I shall now turn back.'

Tripitaka at once began bowing low, hitting his head on the holy ground.

'If you are going to do that all the way up,' said Monkey, 'there will not be much of your head left by the time we get there!'

So Tripitaka stopped bowing and they climbed some way, walking easily. Then they came to a fast-moving river with rough water.

Tripitaka said, 'This cannot be the way.' But then he saw a bridge and a sign which said *Cloud Reach Bridge*. When they came to the bridge, they saw that it was just some trees laid end to end. It was only a little wider than a man's hand.

'Monkey!' cried Tripitaka, afraid. 'I cannot walk across that!'

'Yes, yes, people walk across it to get to the Buddha. Wait while I show you how!'

Dear Monkey! He walked confidently up to the bridge, leapt lightly on to it and was soon waving from the other side.

'Follow me!' he shouted back.

But Pigsy and Sandy repeated to themselves, 'It cannot be done.' Tripitaka did not move at all.

Monkey leapt back again and started pulling at Pigsy. 'Fool, follow me across!' But Pigsy lay flat on the ground and refused to move.

'If you do not come, how will you ever become a Buddha?' said Monkey.

'Buddha or no Buddha,' answered Pigsy, 'I will not go on that bridge!'

As they all started arguing, a boatman appeared with a boat. He was shouting, 'Who wants to cross the river?' But when the boat came nearer, they saw that it had no bottom.

Monkey, with his sharp eyesight, had recognised the boatman as the Bringer of Souls, but he did not tell the others.

'How *can* you take people across a river in a bottomless boat?' asked Tripitaka.

'Many pilgrims ask me that,' he answered. 'But since the beginning of time I have carried too many souls to count.'

'Get in the boat, Master,' said Monkey. 'You will find that it will carry you quite easily and pleasantly.'

But Tripitaka still did not get in, so Monkey pushed him into the boat and Tripitaka immediately fell out into the water. The boatman caught him and pulled him in again. He sat there, unhappily squeezing the water out of his clothes and complaining to Monkey, who had more important things to think about.

Monkey put Pigsy, Sandy and the white horse on the side of the boat with Tripitaka.

The boat left and the boatman had taken them some way down the river when they saw a body in the water. Tripitaka looked very frightened.

Monkey laughed. 'Don't be frightened, Master,' he said. 'That is you.'

And Pigsy cried, 'It *is* you, it *is* you!'

The boatman said the same words to Tripitaka, adding, 'There *you* go! Congratulations!'

Safe on the other side of the river, Tripitaka stepped out of the boat. His earthly body was gone now, gone into the river, and all the foolishness of his early years was washed away. He now had the highest wisdom, the Wisdom of the Far Side of the River, and there is no end to that wisdom.

Before they could thank him, the boatman and his boat had disappeared, and now Monkey explained who the boatman was. Tripitaka began thanking his followers for all they had done for him, but Monkey interrupted.

'We should all give thanks to each other,' he said. 'This journey was too difficult for one man alone, and without all of us the Master could not lose his human body.'

With a strange feeling of lightness and great happiness, they went up the Holy Mountain. Near the top, Immortals greeted the pilgrims and then they were met by the Keeper of Metal, Wood, Water, Fire and Earth.

'So you are here at last, Great Priest,' he smiled.

'Your follower Hsüan Tsang, the priest Tripitaka, has finally arrived,' said Tripitaka, bowing.

The Great Buddha was very pleased at the news and ordered all the Gods to come to him. Then his command was shouted for everyone to hear: 'The priest of T'ang must be brought in.'

Tripitaka, Monkey, Pigsy and Sandy all went in, followed by the white horse and the luggage. In the Great Hall they first lay flat in front of Buddha, then bowed to the right and to the left.

Then Tripitaka said, 'The follower of Buddha, Hsüan Tsang, has come by order of the Emperor of the great land of T'ang to fetch the True Scriptures. They will save all the people of the world. I ask the Great Buddha for these Scriptures and also to allow me a quick return to my own country.'

Then the Great Buddha said these words: 'In all your great Eastern Land there is killing and lying; there are bad thoughts and bad actions. But I have three baskets of Scriptures that can save the people. One contains the Law, which tells of Heaven. One contains the Lessons, which tell of Earth. One contains the Scriptures, which save the Dead. They are written in fifteen thousand one hundred and forty-four books. They are the Path to Perfection, the gate that leads to True Good. In them you can learn everything about men, birds, animals, flowers, trees, stars and Earth. I would like to give them all to you. But the people of China are too foolish to understand them. So a few books from each basket will be given to these priests to take back to the East.'

The pilgrims were taken to a lower room and shown the books from each basket. Then they were given food of a beauty and taste that was unknown on Earth. When they had finished eating, two followers of Buddha took them to a special room down some stairs. The door was opened and a magic light filled the room. On the many beautiful jewelled boxes were written the names of the holy books. The two followers of Buddha led Tripitaka to the place where the Scriptures lay. After inviting him to study the titles, they asked Tripitaka to show them the gifts he had brought for them. They planned to give him the Scriptures in return.

'I have brought nothing at all for you,' said Tripitaka. 'On my journey I have sometimes received gifts, but nobody has ever asked for gifts in return.'

And Monkey, hearing these words, shouted angrily, 'Come with me, Master! We will see what Buddha says about this!'

One of the two followers said quickly, 'There is no need to shout. Come here and fetch your Scriptures.'

The pilgrims hid their anger, put the Scriptures on the horse's back and bowed to Buddha's followers. Then they left, down the mountain.

The Buddha of the Past was sitting in an upper room and had heard everything the two followers had said. He was sure they had given the pilgrims Scriptures with nothing written on them because they had received no gifts. So he sent a messenger after the pilgrims and, of course, the Buddha of the Past was correct. When the pilgrims opened the Scriptures, they saw only white pages.

Tripitaka cried, 'How can I go back to the Emperor of T'ang with these? He will think I am laughing at him. He will order my death.'

'I know the reason for this. Those two followers did not get any gifts, so you did not get any Scriptures! We will have to go back to Buddha,' said Monkey.

They went back at once.

'Listen to this!' shouted Monkey to Buddha. 'They have given us white pages with no words on them because we did not bring them gifts.'

'You need not shout,' said Buddha, smiling. 'I have sometimes thought that perhaps it should not be too easy to get the Scriptures. My two followers expected a gift because of a bad experience they had. Not long ago, I gave them permission to go down the mountain with some Scriptures. After letting Chao read a few Scriptures to his people, my followers were given only some rice in return. The result of hearing these Scriptures was that his people were protected from all their enemies. Afterwards I told my two followers that they had sold the Scriptures too cheaply. So, you see, they are not to blame. In fact, these white pages *are* the True Scriptures. But the people of China are not very clever, so they cannot understand such things. You had better have some scriptures with writing on them.'

This time Tripitaka offered the two Buddhist followers the only gift he could think of – his golden bowl. He had received this bowl from the Emperor of China, who told him to use it for collecting money from kind people on his journey. The followers accepted the gift, but many of the Gods laughed because it was such a small present.

As they started to leave again, the Goddess Kuan-yin appeared in front of Buddha. 'I found this man for you and he has now fetched the Scriptures. It took him five thousand and forty days. The number of chapters in the Scriptures is five thousand and forty-eight. Please allow him to make the return journey in eight days. Then the numbers will be the same.'

'That is a good idea,' said Buddha. 'I will make sure that it is done.'

Buddha then sent for eight of his messengers and said to them, 'Use your magic powers and carry Tripitaka back to the East. When he has left the Scriptures, bring him back here. All of this must be done in eight days.'

Buddha's messengers went immediately to put Tripitaka and the pilgrims on a magic cloud. And as the pilgrims flew away, they had little idea of what was going to happen next.

6.1 Were you right?

Look at your answers to Activity 5.4. Then look at the pictures in Chapter 5 again and circle the right answers below.

1 Pigsy is transformed into a little girl …

a to save a child's life.　　　　**b** to trick Much Gold.

2 When the ice breaks on the river, Monkey leaps into the air but Tripitaka …

a dies in the icy water.　　　　**b** is taken to the Great King's palace.

3 The turtle wants to …

a take the pilgrims across the river.　**b** kill Monkey.

4 The Golden-Headed Immortal welcomes Tripitaka and his followers to …

a Buddha's Jade Temple.　　　　**b** the Great King's underwater palace.

6.2 What more did you learn?

Who do these sentences describe? Write the numbers of the sentences under the right pictures.

A　　　　　　　　B　　　　　　　　C

....　　　　　　　................　　　　　　　................

1 His earthly body has gone into the river and he now has the Wisdom of the Far Side of the River.

2 He shouts angrily at Buddha's followers because they ask for gifts.

3 He thinks the Emperor of T'ang will want to kill him if he returns with Scriptures that are only white pages.

4 He explains that the white pages are the True Scriptures.

5 He offers his golden bowl to Buddha's two followers.

6.3 **Language in use**

Read the sentences in the box. Then complete the sentences below.

> He **used to** live in a little pool in my garden.
>
> His palace below the river **used to** be mine.

1 Tripitaka used to be a foolish man, but now ....

   ....

2 Ch'en's family and the other villagers used to ....

   ...., but now ....

3 The turtle ....,

   but now ....

6.4 **What happens next?**

Read the title of Chapter 6 and the sentences in *italics* below it. Then look at the pictures in this chapter. What do the creatures below want? Do they get it? What do you think? Make notes.

	What do they want?	Do they get it?
1 Pigsy		
2 Sandy Priest		
3 Tripitaka		
4 Monkey		
5 the horse		
6 the turtle		

The End of the Journey

'Hey!' said Pigsy. 'You have just made the others Buddhas.
Why am I not a Buddha too?'

Many Protectors had watched over Tripitaka and his followers on their frightening but wonderful journey to the West. Now the Protectors appeared to Kuan-yin.

'We wish to report that we have followed your holy orders. And, without his knowledge, we have protected the young Priest of T'ang on his journey to the West.'

'I would like to know,' said the Goddess, 'how the pilgrims behaved on their journey.'

'They were brave, they never gave up, and they never forgot the importance of their work. They had many problems along the way – too many to tell. But we have a record of the most difficult fights.'

The Protectors then read to the Goddess Kuan-yin a list of all the fights that the pilgrims had fought. They had fought on their journey against animals, humans and spirits.

Kuan-yin read the list slowly and carefully: 'Tripitaka falls into a hole and is attacked by a tiger, but is saved by his follower Monkey ...' She finished with Tripitaka losing his human body when he stepped into the bottomless boat.

'In our religion, nine times nine is a very important number. You have listed eighty fights,' said the Goddess. 'That is one short of the holy number of eighty-one. There has to be one more fight, so please arrange it.'

When the Goddess had spoken, the Protectors immediately stopped the magic wind that was carrying the pilgrims through space. Suddenly, and without any warning, the horse, the Scriptures, the Master, Monkey, Sandy and Pigsy all fell down to Earth.

Tripitaka looked very surprised to find himself standing on the ground instead of flying through the air.

Pigsy laughed and laughed. 'Well, you never know what is going to happen next, do you?' he said. 'One minute we are rushing at great speed; the next minute we have both feet on the ground.'

Sandy said, 'I think that it was very thoughtful of them. They probably thought we would like a rest.'

'Well,' said Monkey, 'if you sit without moving for ten days, then surely you will speed down nine waterfalls in one day.'

'That is enough rubbish!' said Tripitaka. 'Will you please try to find out where we are.'

'I know, I know,' said Sandy, looking around. 'Listen to that sound of water.'

'It makes Sandy feel at home,' said Monkey.

'It must be ...' Pigsy started to say, but Sandy interrupted him.

'It is the River That Leads to Heaven and this is the western riverbank,' Sandy said.

'I recognise it now,' said Tripitaka. 'On the other side is Mr Ch'en's farm, where you saved the boy and the girl from the Great King. They were very grateful to us and wanted to build a boat for us. In the end, the turtle carried us across. I remember that on this side there are no houses at all. How are we going to manage this time?'

'A trick like this from humans is to be expected,' said Pigsy. 'But not from Buddha's own followers. Buddha told them to take us straight back to China. What do they mean by dropping us in the middle of the journey? They have left us in a difficult situation.'

'I do not know what you two are complaining about,' said Sandy. 'The Master is not a common mortal now. We saw his earthly body go past us down the Cloud River. He will not sink into the water this time. With all three of us to help him, he will surely be able to get across.'

Monkey smiled to himself. 'It is not going to be as easy as that,' he said.

Why did Monkey say that it was not going to be easy? They had enough magic power to cross a thousand rivers! But Monkey knew that the number 'nine times nine' had not yet been reached. He knew that Buddha expected one more fight.

They walked along slowly, wondering what to do. Suddenly, they heard a voice saying, 'Priest of T'ang, Priest of T'ang, come over here.'

As there was nobody on land and no boat on the river, they were very surprised. But suddenly a large white head appeared in the water.

'Well,' called the turtle, 'I have been waiting for you all this time.'

'We are very glad to meet you,' said Monkey. 'Come a little closer.'

Once again, the turtle came out of the river. Monkey led the white horse and then the pilgrims, carrying their luggage, on to its back. Pigsy sat behind its tail, Tripitaka stood on one side of its head and Sandy on the other. Monkey stood with one foot on its neck and the other on its head.

Monkey cried, 'Time to go, Old Turtle! Go gently!' And the turtle swam easily through the endless waters until evening came.

But when they were nearly at the far side, the turtle suddenly asked Tripitaka an important question. 'When I took you across last time, I asked you to find out from Buddha how long I have to wait before I become a human. Did you remember to ask Buddha?'

Unfortunately, Tripitaka had been so busy with his own problems – losing his mortal body, going up the mountain, meeting Buddha and all his followers, taking the Scriptures – that he had had no time to think of anything else.

Tripitaka did not want to tell a lie but he did not know what to say.

When no answer came, the turtle knew that he had not asked. It was very annoyed. The turtle did not think it had asked for much. And it was true, it had not.

'You have broken your promise!' said the turtle. Without another word, it dived deep down into the water, leaving the four pilgrims, the horse and the holy Scriptures in the river.

But there was some good fortune in their misfortune. First, Tripitaka was now immortal and could not die under water. Second, the white horse was really a dragon and could swim very well. Third, Pigsy and Sandy were both perfectly happy in the water. Monkey, of course, just leapt into the air and helped his Master back to the land.

But the Scriptures and all the luggage were wet, and as they climbed to the riverbank a great wind began to blow. The sky grew black and lightning lit up the sky. Tripitaka held the Scriptures close to him while Sandy held the luggage and Pigsy held the white horse.

Monkey knew that this storm was caused by demons who were trying to steal the Scriptures. The demons attacked all through the night, stopping only when the sun began to come up. And although nobody could see them, Monkey hit out with his cudgel at them, holding it in both hands and hitting first to the right and then to the left.

Tripitaka, who was already wet from the storm, was left shaking with fear.

'Monkey,' he asked in a shocked voice, 'what does all this mean?'

'It is jealousy,' answered Monkey. 'The success of our journey has put jealousy in the heart of every demon in Heaven and on Earth, because our power is almost as great as theirs now. It is good that you kept the Scriptures close to you. That and my cudgel saved us from losing the holy words.'

Tripitaka then understood and he thanked Monkey for his protection.

When the sun was hotter, they dried their clothes and the Scriptures on a rock. Even today this rock is called The Rock Where the Scriptures Were Dried. They also dried their shoes and clothes.

When they had almost finished, some workers came past. They said, 'Are you not the gentlemen who crossed the river to fetch the Scriptures from India?'

'That is right,' said Pigsy. 'How do you recognise us?'

'We are from Mr Ch'en's farm,' they answered.

'How far is it from here?' Pigsy asked.

'If you went about twenty kilometres south from here, you would come to it,' they answered.

'Let's take the Scriptures and dry them at the farm,' said Pigsy. 'If we go there, we can sit down comfortably and get something to eat.'

'I am not going,' said Tripitaka. 'We can dry the scriptures very well here.'

But then Mr Ch'en himself appeared. 'I see that you have got the Scriptures,' he said happily. 'Please come home with me!'

'Wait until our Scriptures are dry,' said Monkey. 'Then we will go home with you.'

'I see that your clothes are wet too. What has happened to you?' asked Mr Ch'en.

Tripitaka explained about the white turtle. When he finished, Mr Ch'en again asked them to follow him home. In the end, Tripitaka accepted the kind offer. But when they were collecting the Scriptures, some of the paper stuck to the rock, and part of the last sheet of paper was lost. That is why it is incomplete today. And still today you can find some writing on the Rock Where the Scriptures Were Dried.

Tripitaka was very upset. 'We were not careful enough,' he said sadly.

'Don't get yourself so upset,' said Monkey. 'These Scriptures are now as they are supposed to be. Heaven and Earth are not more complete. The missing part is a secret and it is not meant to be read by others. You were as careful as you needed to be. You did nothing wrong.'

Back at the farm, they were welcomed by everybody there, young and old, and given all the best wine and food. As a Buddha, though, Tripitaka had lost his taste for earthly food, and Monkey wanted only fruit. Sandy ate very little, and even Pigsy ate less than he had before.

'I do not know why I cannot eat more,' he said sadly.

After they had eaten, Mr Ch'en said, 'We have had some pictures painted of you. We wanted to thank you for saving War Boy and Much Gold.' Then War Boy and Much Gold came into the room and bowed. The pilgrims were invited to look at pictures of themselves in the upstairs room of the farm.

'Yours is very like you,' said Pigsy, pushing his elbow gently into Monkey's side.

'I think yours is wonderfully like you too,' said Sandy to Pigsy. 'But the Master's painting is a little too handsome, really.'

'I think it is very good,' said Tripitaka.

The brothers Ch'en and all their workers prayed to these pictures every day.

Since their prayers had started, there had been no more damage from rain and everybody had had plenty to eat.

'That is a gift from Heaven, not from us,' said Monkey. 'But we will certainly try to protect you. You will have many children and those children will have many children. Your animals will grow fat, and the wind and the rain will come at the right time of year.'

The people thanked him again. And again they offered more fruit and cake.

'It is my bad luck,' said Pigsy. 'I used to be able to eat a lot, but in those days no one pushed food on me. Now I eat very little and everybody wants to see me eat more!' Because he did not want to insult the Ch'en family, Pigsy managed to eat eight or nine dishes of vegetables and twenty or thirty cakes.

It was now late at night. Tripitaka watched the Scriptures but he felt nervous. 'I think we should leave,' he told Monkey. 'If we stay here too long, people will try to get our secrets from us.'

'I agree with you,' said Monkey. 'We had better go quietly while everyone is still asleep.'

Pigsy was not a fool now. Sandy and the horse clearly saw the need to go too. And as the pilgrims left the farm, a sweet-smelling wind took them up and away on a cloud.

In the morning, the villagers came again with offers of fruit and other special food. It was a terrible surprise when they found that the pilgrims had disappeared. They looked everywhere for them, but after a few hours they gave up hope.

'Why have you taken our living Buddha away?' they cried to the God of Continuing Days.

Since that time, four times a year, the villagers have performed a special dance in front of the pictures of the Master and his followers. The farm has been turned into a temple and at every hour of every day there are people praying on their knees there. Some pray for better health, some pray for protection on a journey and others pray for their children's future.

Less than a day after they left Ch'en's farm, the pilgrims could see in the distance the towers of Ch'ang-an. It was thirteen years and nine months since Tripitaka had departed.

The Emperor had ordered a high tower to be built outside the western gates and had named it the Scripture Lookout Tower. And now, looking out, he suddenly saw the whole western sky fill with a magic light. A minute later, he noticed a sweet smell in the wind.

The Protectors went with the pilgrims as far as the gates of the city.

'We prefer to wait here for you,' they said to Tripitaka. 'The people around here are very tricky. We do not want them to know that we are here. And there is no need for your followers to go with you. But you, Master, had better go at once and give the Emperor the Scriptures. We will wait for you here and then we will all go back and report to Buddha's Holy Mountain.'

'That sounds fine,' said Monkey. 'But how can the Master carry the Scriptures and who is going to lead his horse? We had better go with him.'

'Kuan-yin promised Buddha that the whole journey would take only eight days. If you all go, Pigsy will be looking around for food, and you will lose time,' said one of the Protectors.

'How can you be so rude?' cried Pigsy. 'Why should I waste time here? I am as anxious as anyone to get back to Buddha's Holy Mountain. The Master has become a Buddha and I intend to become a Buddha too. You wait here. When we have given the Emperor the Scriptures, I will go back with you and will get my reward.'

Then, with Pigsy carrying the luggage, Sandy leading the horse and Monkey at Tripitaka's side, they stopped in front of the tower.

The Emperor and his ministers came down to meet them.

'So my dear brother has come at last!' the Emperor cried, giving him a horse to ride into the city.

When they were seated in the Great Hall, the Scriptures were put in front of the Emperor. Tripitaka told the story of how he arrived at the Holy Mountain. He told of the trick played by Buddha's two followers. He described how he had, in the end, got the written Scriptures by giving his golden bowl as a gift.

'There are, in total, five thousand and forty-eight chapters,' he added.

The Emperor was very happy and he ordered a banquet. Suddenly, he noticed the three pilgrims, who were sitting at the far end of the Hall. He thought they looked unusual.

'I suppose these gentlemen are foreigners?' said the Emperor.

'My oldest follower, named Monkey,' said Tripitaka, 'came from the Cave of the Water Curtain on the Mountain of Flowers and Fruit. Five hundred years ago he made trouble in Heaven and Buddha sent him to a stone prison under a mountain. But he became a holy man with the help of the Goddess Kuan-yin. I was able to free him and take him with me as my follower. He protected me on the journey to India and he helped me to get the Scriptures. Without him, I would not be here now.

'My second follower, Pigsy, came from the Cloud-Ladder Cave and was at the farm of Mr Kao when I found him. He has carried the luggage all through our travels and he was very helpful when we had to get across rivers.

'My third follower, Sandy, came from the River of Sands. He too was brought to me by the Goddess Kuan-yin. And our horse is not the one that you gave to me.'

'Really?' said the Emperor. 'It looks the same to me. Why did you change horses?'

'Actually,' said Tripitaka, 'my first horse was eaten by this one. But Monkey went to Kuan-yin and the Goddess explained that this horse was really a son of the Dragon King of the Western Ocean. He got into some trouble, but he took me to the West and so his life was saved. He has carried me well, over the most difficult hills and mountains. On the way there, I rode on its back; on the way home, it carried the Scriptures. As you can imagine, we are all very grateful to him.'

'You have been served well. Tell me,' said the Emperor, 'how far is it to India?'

'I know only that the summer turned to winter fourteen times. There was no day when we did not ride over hills or mountains. Often we rode through large forests or crossed great rivers and we passed through too many countries to count.'

When the banquet was ready, the Emperor asked, 'Do your followers know how to behave at an Emperor's banquet?'

'I am afraid that they do not,' said Tripitaka. 'They have spent their time mostly in rough country conditions.'

'Don't worry,' said the Emperor. 'I will not blame them. Tell them to come to the banquet.'

There was dancing and singing and music and food at the banquet, and it was a very happy day. In the evening, when the meal ended, the pilgrims went to Tripitaka's old temple in the woods. There the priests welcomed them with a bow.

This time, inside the temple, Pigsy did not shout for more food and Monkey and Sandy behaved perfectly. All three were now Spirits of Wisdom, and it was not difficult for them to stay quiet. When night came, they all went to sleep.

Early next morning, the Emperor woke and called for his secretaries.

'All night I could not sleep because I was thinking of good enough words to thank my brother for his success. I have now, in my head, a few sentences, although they are nothing compared to the wisdom of the Scriptures.'

He asked the secretaries to write down his words, which later became known to all as the Introduction to Buddha's Holy Teachings.

The Emperor then asked Tripitaka to read from some of the Holy Scriptures in the holiest temple in the city. As the Scriptures were so valuable, the Emperor ordered his secretaries to make copies, which were later sent to every city in China.

As Tripitaka started reading, he smelled the sweet wind and the Protectors appeared in the air above the pilgrims. They said, 'You must all leave the Scriptures and follow us to the West.'

At once Monkey and the others, including the white horse, got up from the ground. Tripitaka put down the Scripture that he had started reading. He was lifted straight up to the Ninth Heaven. The Emperor and his ministers bowed low to the ground as they were carried away.

Later, all the people of the city prayed and read the Great Scriptures, and their lives were much better after that.

The four pilgrims and the white horse were taken back to Buddha's Holy Mountain by the Protectors. There they found that their great journey had taken just eight days. On the Holy Mountain they and all the Gods waited for Buddha.

When everyone was ready, Buddha appeared and spoke first to Tripitaka.

'Holy priest,' he said, 'in a past life you were close to me and you were called Golden Tree. But because you did not obey my teaching, you had to start life again in the East. Now you have obeyed me so well that I am making you a Buddha. Your title will be Buddha of Ability.

'Monkey, because you made trouble in Heaven, you were put under the Mountain of Metal, Wood, Water, Fire and Earth. Fortunately, when your time there was finished, you turned your heart to religion, to the fight against wrong-doing and the fight for good. On your recent journey you have done so well that I am making you a Buddha. You will be the Buddha of Success in Difficult Times.

'Pigsy, you were a soldier of the water armies of Heaven. But at a banquet you drank too much and insulted a goddess. And for this you were born again in the human world, looking very much like an animal. When you were living at the Cloud-Ladder Cave, you found religion and offered your protection to Tripitaka on his journey. You are still greedy, but because you carried the luggage all the way, I am now making you the Keeper of the Holy Temple.'

'Hey!' said Pigsy. 'You have just made the others Buddhas. Why am I not a Buddha too?'

'Because,' answered Buddha, 'your conversation and appearance are still not fine enough and you still eat too much. But I have so many followers in the world that you will get plenty to eat in your new job. You will have nothing to complain about.'

Pigsy knew that he had to accept his new job. He did not say another word.

'Sandy, you were a great spirit, but at a banquet you broke a dish of great value and you were sent to the human world. There you lived in the River of Sands and you hungrily ate people. But after that you found religion. You promised to protect and help Tripitaka, and you did. Because of this, I am lifting you high among us and giving you the title of Golden-Bodied Soldier.'

Sandy bowed. Happily, he accepted his new title.

Then Buddha turned to the white horse. 'You,' he said, 'were a child of the Dragon King of the Western Ocean, but you disobeyed your father and were guilty of bad behaviour. Fortunately, you found religion. Because you carried Tripitaka to the West, and the Holy Scriptures on the return journey, you too must have your reward. From this day, you will be one of the eight Heavenly Dragons.'

The white horse made a sign to show how grateful it was. It was led to the back of the Holy Mountain, where there was the Pool of Magic Dragons, and it was pushed into the pool. After a short time, it began to change shape and its coat began to change to a golden colour. Its four feet rested on the clouds and then it flew up out of the pool. It was now changed from a horse to a magic dragon.

'Master,' said Monkey to Tripitaka, 'I am now a Buddha, like you. I should not have to wear a cap so that you can control me.'

'It was put on you,' said Tripitaka, 'at a time when you knew nothing. Then we needed to control you. Now you are a Buddha and it has gone. Feel your head and you will see. It is not there now.'

Monkey put his hand on his head. Tripitaka was right; the cap had gone. A grateful smile spread across his face.

All the spirits of Heaven watched as Tripitaka, Monkey, Pigsy, Sandy and the horse received their new, holy titles. While they went to their places in the Great Hall, many loud voices began to pray to them. They were accepted with open arms. And from that day, Pigsy did not shout for more food and Monkey and Sandy behaved perfectly. The reason for this was simple. All three had received the greatest of gifts – wisdom.

I give this, my book, to you, dear reader, so you can understand the beauty of Buddha's Land. It will be a reward for kindness, and it will help with the suffering of the lost souls of this world. I would like to think that my readers will turn their hearts towards the True Way, and will be born again in the World of True Happiness.

1 Seated in the Great Hall with the Emperor, Tripitaka is telling him about getting the Scriptures. Monkey, Pigsy and Sandy join in. Work with four other students and have this conversation.

Student A You are Tripitaka. Introduce your followers to the Emperor. Talk about your journey, and let your followers tell their stories.

Student B You are Monkey. Talk about yourself and some of the fights.

Student C You are Pigsy. Talk about the trouble you had at Mr Kao's farm and how the journey has changed you.

Student D You are Sandy. Talk about the nine heads and the Goddess Kuan-yin's help during the journey.

Student E You are the Emperor. Ask Tripitaka and his followers questions about their journey, and get as much information as possible.

2 Look at the pictures below. Discuss these questions with other students.

1 What was the crime that each was punished for? Do you feel sorry for any of them? Why?

2 What rewards did they receive from Buddha? Why? Was Buddha fair to Pigsy, do you think?

3 What did they learn from their journey?

4 Who do you think Tripitaka felt most grateful to? Why?

5 If you could be one of the pilgrims, which one would you prefer to be? Why?

6 What do you know about Buddhism? Is it a religion that interests you? Why (not)?

Monkey has asked you to sell his cudgel, cap and spell, and magic hairs on the Internet. Write a description of each, including its use and some information about its history, and give the selling price.

For Sale

cudgel
Price
....

cap and spell
Price
....

magic hairs
Price
....

1 **Work with another student. When you think of monkeys, what do you think of? Tick (✓) the boxes.**

2 **Read this story about some very special monkeys.**

Did you know that there are very small monkeys from Central and South America who help people with serious physical problems? The monkeys are sent to live in human families when they are babies and later go to a training school. They are intelligent, can follow commands and are very good at using their hands to do many different kinds of jobs. Because they like being with people, they can happily live in a house.

The monkeys are trained to use a toilet and take baths. They are also trained to fetch things, prepare meals, move a person's arms or legs, turn lights on and off, put reading glasses in the right position on a person's face and turn the pages of a book. They learn to turn on the computer, the TV and other similar machines. They learn well between the ages of fifteen to twenty-five and they live to be thirty or forty years old. They give a wonderful service that makes it possible for these people to live in their own homes.

Use the Internet and learn more about these 'capuchin monkeys'. Then discuss with the same partner whether monkeys should be used in this way. What are the advantages and/or disadvantages to humans and monkeys?

3 Discuss ways in which animals are used by these people. Write which animals are used and your opinion of this use of animals.

Who uses animals	Which animals?	Your opinion
Scientists		
Blind people		
Entertainers		
Hunters		
Police		

4 Buddhists believe that it is wrong to hurt or kill animals. But they also recognise that medical testing on animals gives humans chances for better health. Which of these sentences do you agree with (✓)? Discuss your answers.

1 ☐ It is never acceptable to use animals for medical testing.

2 ☐ It is important and necessary to use animals for this purpose.

3 ☐ It is acceptable only when there is no other choice.

4 ☐ It is acceptable only when the animal is looked after kindly.

6 ☐ It is acceptable only when the animal is not killed.

7 ☐ It is acceptable for animals to suffer or die for this purpose.

5 **Work with a number of other students.**

a Imagine that you are very clever monkeys. You know that you are going to be used for medical testing. Plan your escape from the medical centre. How will you trick the humans who are keeping you there?

b Plan a computer game using your escape plan. How is it played? Do the monkeys or the humans win? Make notes below.

Notes

c Write a radio advertisement for your game. Think first about these questions.

What is the name of the game?

Who are the main characters and what are their plans?

What sound effects will you use in the advertisement?

Why should people buy it?

Where can people buy your game?

....

....

....

....

....

....

....

....